Growing
LOCAL FOOD

Empowering you and your community to grow more of your own food

> After a rewarding, but often frustrating career as a General Practitioner, where the life expectancy of a medical doctor is 57 years, Dr. Mary Lou Shaw has found her voice and a way to treat the causes and not just the symptoms of so many of our food related diseases and bad eating habits. In her book, *Growing Local Food,* she and her husband, Tom, have clearly charted the path to a healthier and more rewarding life through simple living and growing their own food on fertile soil.
>
> —*Art Bolduc*

Mary Lou Shaw

Unless otherwise noted all photographs are taken by the author on her farm.

ISBN 10: 1-933753-25-0
ISBN 13: 978-1-933753-25-6

Book Design by Rosetta Mullet

Printed on 50% recycled paper post consumer waste in the USA by Carlisle Printing of Walnut Creek

2673 Township Road 421
Sugarcreek, Ohio 44681

Carlisle Press
WALNUT CREEK

phone | 800.852.4482

Dedication

To my husband, Tom, whose values and hard work make our little farm possible, and to our daughter, Justine, the culinary genius who creates our favorite recipes.

Introduction

Henry Thoreau said, "There are a thousand people hacking at the branches of a problem to one who is striking at the root." In this book, Growing Local Food, Mary Lou Shaw puts the ax to the root, and gently shows us that there is a better way of eating than buying processed foods saturated with the ubiquitous high fructose corn syrup and other questionable additives available at the supermarket.

As a physician, Dr. Shaw has firsthand experience with the results of unhealthy food, which show up as obesity, diabetes, high blood pressure and heart disease. She is also keenly aware of the damage done to the environment in the production of these "cheap" foods and that they are not always "safe" foods.

At least several times a year the news of an E.coli outbreak hits the paper. Oftentimes in tainted ground beef where the meat from hundreds of animals is blended, but also in vegetables such as lettuce, and its source of contamination is often hard to track down.

In this book a way of producing milk and meat, vegetables and honey is shown that is not only safer and more nutritious, but better tasting.

Nicely arranged in twenty-two fairly short chapters, Mary Lou's knowledge of gardening and farming is clearly evident as she covers everything from the soil, seeds, planting and growing, and then the harvest and the preservation of the season's production.

On the Shaw farm, food travels only yards before being served on the table and we would likely all agree that quality of life begins with good food. But then food is more than just nourishment for the body; it is also mealtime when family and friends and even strangers gather around the table to share in the goodness of the fields and gardens. If you are tired of eating second-rate fare, Mary Lou Shaw shows you how you can change that and understand that good farming means good food, and how you can do it yourself.

—David Kline

Prologue

I grow my own food now. I am a homesteader, a wife, a mother, a neighbor and hopefully a good steward of the land. I am also a physician, and it is in that role that I became concerned about our health, our food and our future.

When I was in medical school in the 1980s, many diseases such as diabetes, obesity, asthma, precocious puberty, Alzheimer's and autism were either extremely rare or limited to specific age groups. These diseases have now grown to epidemic proportions.

The corporate response to a sicker population is to look for cures through more technology and pharmaceuticals. Many of us, however, are looking for ways to again find healthful food and restore a healthy environment as means to prevent these diseases. We want local food so we can assure ourselves that it is grown without poisons. We also want local food to help decrease our dependency on petroleum. We see locally grown food as better for our health, the health of our communities and the health of our planet.

If you've never gardened before, where do you begin? Well, I have been gardening most of my life, but I'm still making plenty of mistakes. If we fear making mistakes, we will never take the first step towards growing our own food. In picking up this book and beginning to foster local foods, you are stepping on a learning curve that will stimulate your brain, bring you closer to nature, challenge your creativity and give you funny stories to tell of your own mistakes. I believe it will also give you greater resiliency for our uncertain future, greater enjoyment at the dinner table, better health and a greater sense of community.

There was so much to learn in medical school that we used to say, "See one, do one, teach one." There is also so much to learn to again grow our food locally. I encourage each of you to have the courage to step forward and begin growing and finding your own local food. None of us are experts. Teach as you learn so that others can also find better health and be better prepared for the future. We do not survive well as individuals, but we can thrive as communities.

—Mary Lou Shaw, M.D.

Contents

We enjoy the view from our backyard. The barn in the meadow is one place the animals can find shelter. The windmill pumps drinking water to four tanks located at different places in the pasture. And the high fences in the foreground keep the two roosters separated as they alternate days exploring the farm with their hens.

Why Local Food
Is Healthier Food

“Buying local allows you to know where your food comes from and how it was grown. It feels good to sit down at the dinner table and give thanks for healthful and delicious food that was grown in your own garden or came from a nearby farm. Besides increasing your dining pleasure, eating food from local sources is a powerful vote for better personal and community health.”

We've heard about organic food for quite awhile, but now it seems that "eating local" is what's being talked about. I don't blame you for rolling your eyes when told there's one more criteria for eating healthfully. It's already tough enough to try to decipher food labels at the store. However, eating foods that are grown locally has such a huge impact on health that I'd love you to share these benefits.

The "fresh produce" we see at the grocery store has such a long journey that it lacks both nutrients and taste. Our other choice is packaged and processed food which is full of additives to give it taste and preserve it. The additives, like high fructose corn syrup, have resulted in obesity, diabetes, high blood pressure and cardiac disease. In other words, non-local, industrialized food is

These Dorking chickens are categorized as "threatened" by the American Livestock Breeds Conservancy (ALBC). They are an excellent backyard bird good for both eggs and meat. When chickens are free to be outdoors to eat grass, weeds and bugs, they produce healthier eggs and meat for you. They also remain free of diseases such as salmonella.

making us sick! This is the reason many communities are gradually growing and distributing locally more of their own food.

It is true that purchasing organic food is an important step towards eating healthier. Buying organic is also important because we vote with our dollars for farming methods that don't contaminate land and water. However, the amount of nutrition our food contains is as important as what poisons it doesn't contain. We want to eat food that is chemical-free, but also food that is "nutrient-dense."

Since the 1950s, the amount of vitamins, minerals and protein in our food has fallen by as much as 50 percent. Some of this decline is because hybrid varieties, which have been developed for higher yields, are actually lower in nutrients. A second important reason is that most soil now lacks the nutrients that plants need to produce nutritious produce. Our food can't be nutrient-dense if the soil they are grown in is nutrient-depleted.

Only when we buy or grow our food locally can we actually be assured of nutritious food. We will be able to choose heirloom varieties of seeds and plants. We can choose not only organic, but sustainably grown food. Sustainable farming means that the health of the soil is being preserved. Growing our own food or knowing how our local farmer raises the food we buy are the only ways I know to be assured that the food we eat is both nutritious and without chemicals.

As we begin to eat this nutritious food, we immediately get the bonus of having delicious produce at our dinner tables. It is delightful to discover that nutritionally dense food is also full of flavor. I smile when people say that I'm a good cook, when I know the secret is the flavor-packed produce from our garden! You'll find that no fancy restaurant will be able to compete for flavor with the food from your garden or farmers' market.

Locally grown food from good soil will also have a big, and very positive, impact on your pocketbook. This isn't surprising when we take into consideration the cost of doctors' visits and pharmaceuticals. Far from being a theoretical consideration, healthful food does result in good health. And why not? This is exactly how nature intended us to eat.

Besides these personal health concerns, buying local food makes our communities healthier. Imagine the amount of money you spend on groceries each month and add this to everyone else's grocery money. If just 40 percent of these dollars could go to local people who grow our food, our communities would become more economically robust for all of us. Spending dollars locally is a good way to vote for healthier communities. Additionally, as gasoline prices go higher and transporting food becomes more expensive, we can individually save money by growing our own food.

A final way local food is healthier is that it's better for our planet. The food we eat is shipped an average of 1500 miles and much of it requires refrigeration along the way. Every gallon of gas we burn puts five pounds of carbon in the atmosphere. We deserve the option of not contributing to this problem. After all, it seems like a good deal to do something to benefit our personal health and have it also result in healthier communities and planet.

My husband and I have gradually been growing more of our own food so that most of what we eat is now from our garden and animals. We began because it's challenging and fun, but the incredible flavor of what we grow at home makes it impossible to return to store-bought food. We are also grateful to avoid the chemicals, hormones, antibiotics and additives that are in processed food.

Many of you might want to get involved in this local food project. You may want to grow, buy, sell, share or trade food in the future. Who knows—you might choose to do a bit of each!

In this book we'll explore how to grow and buy food in your own community. Learning how to grow healthful food will allow you to grow your own food. These same concepts can help you find the farmers you can trust to grow your food. You'll be equipped with the questions you need to judge if the soil, plants, produce and animals were nurtured in a way to give you the best food possible.

Let's get smarter about what makes food *good* and how we can again get control of what we eat.

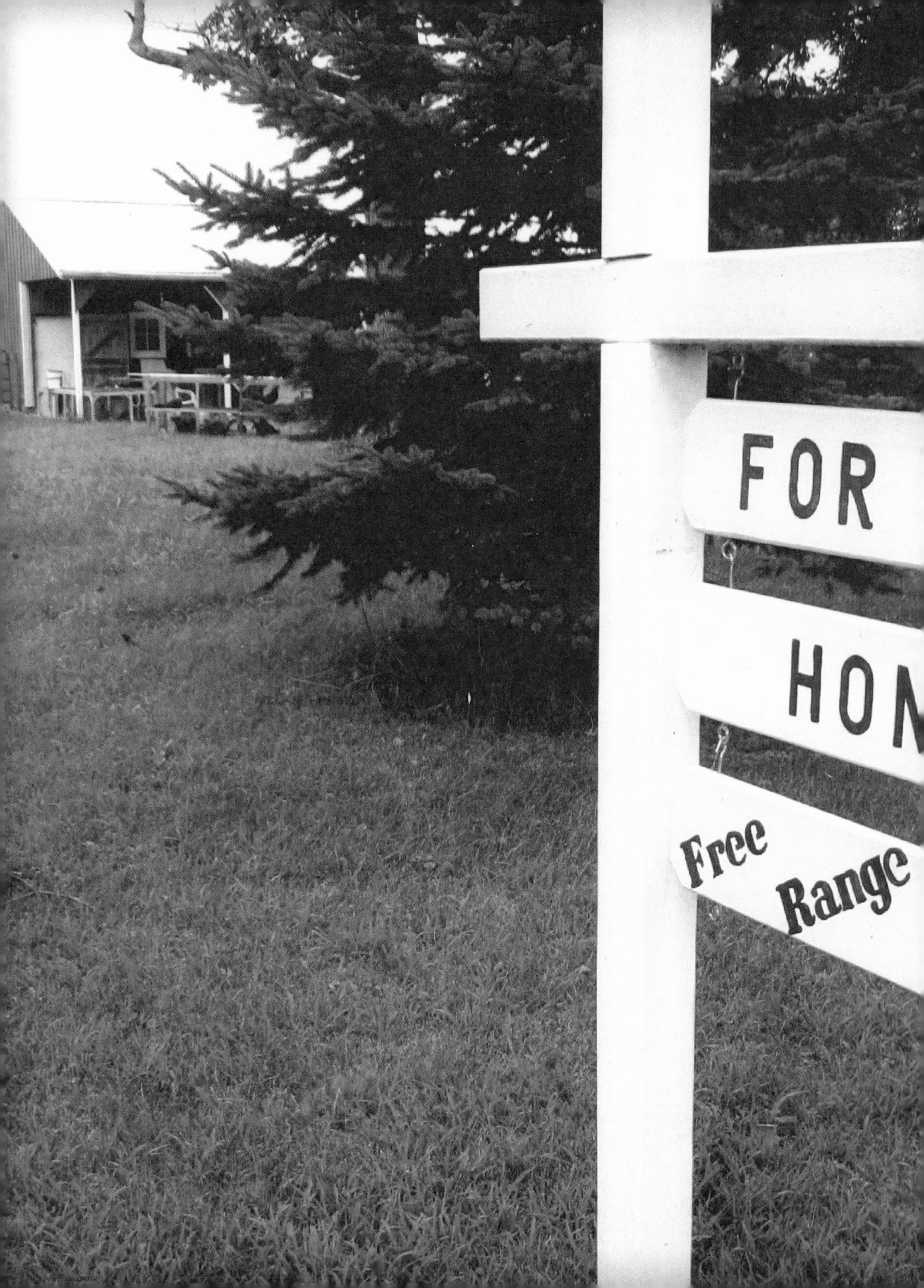
FOR
HON
Free
Range

Where You Can Find Local Food

We don't all have land on which to grow food, but we all have the need for both food and community. You may begin with a pot of herbs on a windowsill or a neighborhood garden created from a vacant lot. You may convert part of your lawn to garden, or be a farmer with hundreds of acres of corn who is only beginning to grow vegetables for your family. We can all be successful if we learn, work and share together.

Those of you who would like to eat food that's grown locally may now be wondering, "Where do we find it?" Let's explore what other communities are doing, so you can discover what food your community already has and see how you can help increase your access to local food.

Farmers' markets have become increasingly popular over the last decade as people seek local, seasonal food. A summer farmers' market is a great way to meet local farmers, try their produce and let them know what you want to buy. A successful market requires faithful consumers who value the hard work of growing, gathering and bringing produce to market.

This produce has many benefits over what you can buy at the grocery store. The produce

Buying your food locally allows you to see how the food is raised. It also encourages local farmers to get into the business of raising the food you want to buy.

at a farmers' market has not been picked before ripening and then packed for long-distance travel. The varieties of produce have been chosen for flavor and not for the durability required for machine-picking and shipping. Buyers can get to know the vendors, what they offer and how their produce was grown. When you find your favorite and want more, local farmers will make the effort to grow it for you.

The benefit to farmers is that they are able to get a fair price for their produce and products. Selling directly to the consumer allows farmers the enjoyment of their buyers' appreciation and the benefit of their comments.

Community Supported Agriculture (CSA) has become popular over the last 20 years. It offers a relationship between local farmers and consumers where local, seasonal food can be bought directly from the farmer. Farmers offer "shares" in their anticipated harvest and the consumer receives weekly, ultra-fresh food throughout the growing season. The farmers have the advantage of knowing their customers, knowing how much food to grow and receiving money at the beginning of the growing season. The consumer gets to know the farmer and has the experience of trying new foods that are packed with vitamins and flavor.

This close relationship between consumer and farmer—to the extent that the risk and cost of growing food is shared—has become popular because people want to know how their food is grown. CSAs encourage local people to grow food for us because it gives them financial support for their endeavors.

Direct farm sales are another means of buying local food, and certainly the best way of seeing where your food comes from. Word of mouth, road signs or newspaper ads may help you find wonderful free-range eggs, honey or grass-fed meat. Resources in the back of this book give online sites to help locate local foods. As you buy more food locally, there will be more farmers willing to grow for a local market.

Buying clubs are springing up across the country as a means for people to buy food as a group. Saving money on food purchases is one reason these groups are popular. Another uniting theme is often the desire to obtain high-quality food. The club can buy in bulk locally produced chicken, beef, eggs, cheese, milk and garden produce. Members can then individually receive the benefit of the lower cost of buying in bulk.

These clubs sometimes choose to own or lease animals such as cows or pigs. Although still cared for by the farmer, the members determine how the animals are raised. The money they spend to buy or lease the animals is returned to the buyers in the animals' produce. In this way, the buyers know that their meat, milk or eggs come from animals that were not only humanely treated, but who were fed in a manner that results in healthful produce.

In general, an ongoing relationship with local farmers allows you to support them in producing the quality of food you value. If you want chemical-free produce, a farmer needs to know you are willing to pay for the labor it takes to manage weeds and pests by hand. If you value grass-fed meat or dairy products, you need to be consistent in your purchases so farmers can rely on having customers for their produce.

The family garden is a wonderful source of local food from your own yard. You are both the farmer and consumer producing food for your own table. This is truly the most pleasurable way of eating.

To help support you in your gardening efforts, the following essays include everything from container gardening, to raised beds, to "edible landscape" and even to a garden large enough to meet most of your family's food needs.

For starters, how about ordering a couple seed catalogs? You may not imagine growing plants from seeds, but there's nothing more enjoyable on a cold winter's evening than curling up with a seed catalog filled with great information and gorgeous photos. Imagine green Provider beans, red Celebrity tomatoes or yellow Sunshine squash! Companies that are listed as resources for the next chapter have beautiful photos and offer organic and heirloom seeds. If you need some inspiration, this is the way to begin.

There is an important worldwide movement to obtain local, fresh, nutritious, affordable food. You'll find it both fun and empowering to get on board.

The Power of Seeds

Imagine taking a single seed, planting it, and then harvesting dozens or even hundreds of seeds that you can then grow, eat and share with others. Seeds give us the power to grow our own food, and watching them grow reminds us of our connection to the earth. Helping to save heirloom seeds by growing and exchanging them reminds us of our connection to future generations.

Those who say they have never witnessed a miracle must never have planted a seed. A tiny tomato seed turns into a large plant loaded with tomatoes; each tomato contains the potential for dozens of offspring. A handful of beans can be put in your soup pot or be planted to grow enough beans for twenty soup pots. Miracles!

As miraculous as seeds are, not all are equal. Heirloom seeds and hybrid seeds appear the same, but their potential is much different. Did you eat a great-tasting tomato and want to save its seed to grow your own? You can only do this if it's an heirloom tomato, or its offspring won't taste or look like what you enjoyed. Hybrids are a cross between two different parent varieties, and their seeds will be any arrangement of their parents' genetics. Surprises aren't always bad, but they're usually not what we had in mind. An heirloom plant always breeds true, and we value them for

(Left to right, top to bottom):
David's Beans, Tiger Eye, Greasy bean,
Lima, Calypso, Turkey Craw
Tiger Eye (lighter shade), Kentucky Wonder
Hidatsa Shield Figure, Midnight Black Turtle

traits that have been handed down through generations—traits like flavor, disease resistance and dependability.

Hybrid seeds are crossed for certain traits, but these are usually traits that make them suitable for mechanical harvesting, shipping and commercial marketing. Characteristics valued are tough skins, attractive fruit and crops that ripen all at once. Some hybrids are delicious, but then I have to keep my fingers crossed that corporations will make their seeds available again.

Besides flavor and dependability, there's another reason I like heirloom plants—I really enjoy having the power to save and share my favorite fruits and vegetables without depending on corporations to sell me seeds each year. When you read the chapter in this book on saving seeds, you'll see that you can have a "sustainable" garden by saving your own seeds. But saving seeds only works if you aren't growing hybrid seeds.

I still grow some hybrid plants from seeds when I am looking for certain disease-resistant varieties. Gardening is a continual learning process, and until I get better at keeping these plants healthy enough to avoid most insect damage, I grow hybrids for assistance. However, with future generations in mind, I know I want to help save heirloom seeds as much as possible, so our children will also be able to grow their own food.

Another reason I avoid buying seeds from large corporations is that I don't want to grow genetically-engineered (GE) food. Giant agribusiness companies have modified the DNA of plants to complement their herbicides and pesticides. There is small-scale laboratory data that GE food is dangerous to consume. Rather than funding more testing to assure GE food is safe to eat, corporations have been allowed to genetically modify almost all the corn, soybeans, canola and sugar beets that is grown in the United States. That means most processed food, although unlabeled, contains GE ingredients. We are an entire generation being experimented on by consuming foreign DNA. It is very difficult to avoid these products, but we have some power to opt out of this experiment by growing our own food with non-GE seed.

There are only a handful of seed companies now. The names of the small companies are still on catalogs, but they have been bought up by large corporations. For example: Gurney's, Vermont Bean Seed, Totally Tomatoes, Selected Seeds and Jung are all one conglomerate. Monsanto has bought Seminis, and Seminis has bought Burpee.

So what's the problem with fewer and larger companies? Besides creating more GE seed, the irreversible problem is the loss of genetics. Even 20 years ago, the smaller companies carried a much larger variety of seeds than we see today. When these companies were purchased, the majority of their varieties were dropped, and the genetics were lost.

People have always relied on a large variety of plants because variety gives resilience. One variety grows better in certain climates or a certain year than another. One is more resistant to a disease or insect than others. The potato famine in Ireland occurred because only one kind of potato was grown, and there was no variety to substitute.

As I get older, I become more concerned with how future generations will get their food. As plant and animal genetics are being rapidly lost, I find it fun and empowering to save seed and share with others. It's cheaper too!

At our house, the names of our saved seeds sound like a family album: David's beans, Alice's peppers and Mr. Prince's corn have been grown for decades by others, and now are treasured by us.

I hesitate to tell you about my bean-fetish! I find dried beans so beautiful and unique. They fill quart jars on the kitchen shelves, showing off their beauty while waiting to become part of our meals. The current lineup includes: Calypso, Cherokee Trail of Tears, Midnight Black Turtle, Masai, David's, Hidatsa Shield Figure, Tiger Eye, Jackson Wonder Limas, Turkey Craw and Greasy. I purchased some from seed companies specializing in heritage seeds and some were precious gifts. When I'm gifted with no more than a dozen beans, they take a couple years of growing to get enough to eat and share.

Organizations like Seed Savers Exchange, begun in 1975, are dedicated to saving seed genetics. This organization and other seed companies dedicated to preserving genetics are listed in the back of this book.

If you're reading this in the wintertime, it's the perfect time to order a seed catalog. Dreaming about your spring garden is the first step to making it happen. If there are seeds now at the store, look through the packages to find something that sounds fun to grow. If you or your children have never planted a seed, it's not important at first to choose heirloom over hybrid. The most important thing is that you witness the miracle of a tiny seed becoming a plant that can bear food for you to eat.

→ 4 ←

Good Food
Needs Good Soil

❝ Perhaps it's because we were told to avoid dirt when we were children that we don't have a natural attraction to it as adults? "Soil," however, should fascinate us! Good soil is alive and capable of producing food that gives us healthy bodies and immune systems. Nurturing soil, so that it's full of nutrients and teeming with life, is an essential part of learning to care for our plants and ourselves. ❞

The main reason we bother eating food that is grown locally is that we want excellent flavor and nutrition. So, let's get down to the basics. Most basic of all is the soil that food is grown in.

We've heard that "you are what you eat." It shouldn't surprise us that fruits and vegetables are made up of what *they* eat. What they "eat" is what they can absorb from the soil they are planted in.

Soil isn't just dirt that holds up our plants. It may have become that in commercial farming, but we want better. We want the soil for our food to contain the nutrients that our bodies need. These nutrients keep us healthy, but they're also what make food taste good.

Perhaps you've been taught to eat certain foods "because they're good for you." Mother Nature is so wise that she makes the most *nutritious*

Spring crops depend on good soil to thrive and so each has been mulched with compost. The garlic in the foreground is planted in the fall, and will be harvested midsummer. The lettuce is planted in early spring. During cold nights, white cloth is placed over hoops to protect it from frost. The perennial rhubarb, in the background, is given compost annually.

food also the most *delicious* food. What a good deal! If we learn how to make our food nutritious, it will also be delicious.

This seems simple—right? We can buy fertilizer in the store whose package has three numbers signifying the amount of nitrogen, potassium (potash) and phosphate in the mix. Plants seem to look good and do well when fed this.

One problem with these fertilizers is that our bodies need most of the vitamins and minerals that the earth contains—not just these three. Nature offers more than 100 nutrients, and we need all of them.

Nature builds a lot of resiliency into plants and even our bodies. This means we can often "get by" without good food until we're challenged with a disease or cancer. That's when having a healthy body and a good immune system really pays off. The basis for excellent health is eating food that has been grown in excellent soil.

The only way I know to get this quality of food is to know *how* our food is grown. This means we know how the local farmer grows it, or we grow it ourselves. Either way, we need to understand how good soil is built so it contains all the nutrients we need.

Soil is a living system. The thin, organic layer on top is where plants grow and tiny animals live. These bacteria, fungi and protozoans decompose potential nutrients and make them available to our plants. Under this layer is the subsoil. The subsoil is inorganic, and contains most of the soil's nutrients. Plants send down their roots into this layer looking for water. Earthworms create the pathways for the plants' roots while they also distribute minerals throughout the soil.

There is so much cooperative life going on in healthy soil! The plants feed these tiny microbes from their own energy stores. In exchange, the microbes make the minerals available to the plants. We become part of the beneficiaries of this system as the nutrients find their way into our food.

Contrary to our years of rototilling, we are now taught to not turn over the soil. It does seem to make sense that the layers of soil shouldn't have to rearrange themselves every year! At our house, unless weeds get way ahead of us, we try not to disturb the soil. We place a layer of mulch on top, and plant in that.

What is mulch? Basically, mulch is organic material (leaves, straw, wood chips) that will hold in moisture in dry times. Mulch also prevents the topsoil from washing away in wet times. More ideally, it also contains nutrients and humus, which holds moisture. Mulch can greatly reduce how much water your garden needs in a dry summer. During heavy rains, mulch can save your topsoil and crops.

The ideal mulch is compost, which is what we use at our house. This organic plant and animal material has already been aerobically decomposed. *Hurrah*—that means the weed seeds have been killed! It also means the nutrients are ready to be absorbed by the plants. Composting is quite a science, and so essential to having nutritious food, that we will talk about it in detail later.

We're also going to talk more about how to garden in small places like containers, existing landscape or raised beds. For those of you who have that in mind, here's a wonderful recipe that can start you out with good soil this spring, without taking years to build up your topsoil:

Buy bags and mix together:
⅓ compost
> *If you can buy compost from two or three different companies, that's ideal.*
> *Different sources result in more variety of nutrients.*

⅓ perlite or vermiculite:
> *I've been told that some vermiculite has been contaminated with asbestos.*
> *I can't verify this, but I buy perlite for that reason.*

⅓ peat moss

This mixture will give you a good start to growing nutritious food. We'll work to get ideal soil in the years ahead, but we don't want to wait for ideal conditions to begin. Eating good food is our goal, and reaching this goal will take many small steps—a love of learning and even a lot of humor at times. All you need to do now is take the first step.

Groceries from Your Own Backyard

❝ Not being able to have a big garden should not stop us from gardening. If there is a corner of space, as well as sunshine and water, we can grow food. The first experience of having cherry tomatoes in a hanging pot, or beans climbing a fence, is thrilling for the whole family. You might be surprised how many neighbors will also be interested. In a few years, your neighborhood could be producing a remarkable amount of food. ❞

We've discussed seeds and soil; now all that remains is to figure out where to put your new garden! I've heard people in town and suburbs say they don't have room for a garden. Plants do need sun, good soil, water and drainage, but they don't necessarily need a lot of room. Here are three suggestions for growing food in small spaces:

Container planting: Do a mental tour of your yard. Do you have a patio or driveway area that gets sunshine at least six hours a day? Visualize the front yard too, because vegetables can be as attractive as shrubs or flowers.

Now imagine what containers you could use. I like clay pots, but large ones might be too heavy to be practical. Plastic containers are attractive and

There are usually many things to harvest from our Ohio garden by late July. Pictured are: sunflowers, tomatoes, cucumbers, storage onions with baby zucchini on their right and bell peppers on their left. Next are carrots, okra, dill, red and white potatoes and red beets. Marigolds (lower right) are planted among the tomatoes to protect them from insect damage.

can last for years. To make deep pots lighter yet, you could place Styrofoam packing peanuts and peat moss at the bottom portion of your pots.

Before filling the containers, make sure they have adequate drainage. If in doubt, don't hesitate to drill a few more holes in the bottom. Next mix equal parts of compost, perlite and peat moss to put in the pots. When planting time comes, your pots will be ready for seeds or small plants.

Vegetables that can be sown directly into containers include kale, garlic, potatoes, beans, peas, cucumbers and carrots. Of all these, carrots will need the deepest container.

Plant a salad mix early: Lettuce, radishes, onions and peas do well in the spring. Herbs can also share space for an aromatic container. Place chives, basil, marjoram, thyme, parsley and sage together. Keep pinching and using them as they grow so they don't become too crowded.

If the only sunny area around your home is lawn, and you don't feel like breaking sod this spring, why not plant directly into bags of good-quality topsoil? I admit that large, plastic bags don't sound like attractive containers, but it's a practical way to make an instant garden. Place the bags of soil flat wherever you want a garden bed. Next, poke drainage holes in the bottom side and cut a large rectangle from the side which has become the top. You can now plant your seeds or seedlings directly in the bag. If using several bags, mulch the paths between with straw or wood chips. When your vegetables are flourishing in July, this arrangement makes an attractive and manageable garden.

Square-foot gardening: Besides planting in bags of soil, there's another way to create gardens on lawns without doing major soil excavation. You can put down heavy-duty landscape cloth and build a raised bed on top of it. Honest—this can be done without a lot of tools or construction know-how.

Begin by purchasing landscape cloth that is heavy enough to prevent grass and weeds from penetrating it. You'll also need four-foot lengths of one-by-four or one-by-six wood. The final items to purchase are screws to connect the wood at right angles. The wood should NOT be treated because you don't want chemicals in your food.

To construct your new garden:
1) Place the cloth in an area that gets sunshine six to eight hours a day.
2) Place the wood on edge to create a square.
3) Screw the corners together.
4) Fill with the compost, perlite and peat moss mixture.

The "square-foot" concept is now created by dividing the soil surface into 16 easy-to-manage, one-foot squares. The dividers can be anything from discarded venetian blinds to wood. Each square foot will "house" a various number of plants—one to 16 plants, depending on how far apart the seed packages tell you to put the seeds. A tomato or cabbage gets one section, but beet or turnip seeds can be thinned to every four inches. Rather than in rows, it's attractive to plant lettuce or chard densely in its square foot—and then thin it as it grows. As you harvest one section, plant something else there.

The idea of a four-by-four raised bed is to allow you to reach in without stepping on the soil. For children, the dimensions should be three-by-three feet. In any garden, try not to step on soil where plants will grow.

Edible landscape: If you have sunny spaces that would benefit from landscaping, consider landscaping with vegetables. Don't picture something plain and ugly—if it's part of your landscape, it has to look good! You could incorporate an arbor or trellis for tomatoes and a tepee for string beans. The ground cover can be basil, zucchini, chard, collards and bell peppers. Author Rosalind Creasy found that the produce from her 100-square-foot "landscaping" was worth $975.18 in a single summer. If this sparks your imagination, you may want to investigate books listed in "Resources."

I like the concept of pots, bags or square-foot gardening for a couple reasons. First, most anyone can begin gardening without needing a lot of land, equipment or muscles. Just as important, these methods allow us to start small. If we plant too much the first year, the weeds and even produce can overwhelm us in July. By beginning small, you can plan how to *enlarge* your garden as you harvest wonderful food this coming summer.

➵ 6 ↢

Gardens Can Be Any Shape or Size

❝Large gardens are a mixed blessing. Although they produce a great amount of produce, they also require a great amount of manual labor. When large families with willing members have room for a big garden, they can produce all the produce they need. When we lack land or many hands, gardening together on common ground is a wonderful solution. Communal gardens work well for all types of communities. ❞

Let's talk about two ends of the garden spectrum—having so large a garden that it doesn't seem manageable; and the opposite, not having any land for a garden or even space for a container of plants. Both problems need solving, because either may result in no food being grown. Let's discuss first how large gardens can be more productive and easier to care for.

For those with large gardens: What do I mean by large? Perhaps I am mostly referring to established gardens that must be walked through to reach the plants. Soil that's walked on is compressed, and so is not optimal for plants. We need to separate walking and growing space.

Besides having separate space for feet and plants, you want your garden to be a place where

This large garden is divided in four quadrants. Flowers are planted among the tomatoes in this quadrant to attract beneficial insects and to add to my gardening enjoyment.

you enjoy spending time. This often means that it is both close to the house, small enough to keep attractive, simple enough to keep paths open and perhaps includes sitting space.

Separate trodden paths and growing areas provide a permanent arrangement for your garden. Consider making your paths from 12 to 18 inches wide. Twelve-inch-wide paths are sufficient for walking. Our garden paths are 18 inches wide because I'm more comfortable with kneeling when planting or weeding. There are no set rules for your design, so create a garden that suits you best.

You don't want to spend time and energy weeding paths. Instead, cover paths with newspaper and layer them with straw. The straw and newspaper gradually break down to become organic material for your garden. Layer them thickly and they'll service you through the growing season.

There's one caution about straw for your garden; Dow Chemical produces a long-acting herbicide, aminopyralid, which can kill your garden plants. It is sold as "Milestone" and "Forefront." It lasts so long that it can still be present in straw and even well-rotted manure. It is responsible for hundreds of home gardens being destroyed in Great Britain and the USA. Your garden and labor are precious. Ask before you bring straw home!

I've talked about walking paths, so now let's discuss growing space. Thirty-inch-wide beds, between walking paths, work well for plants. These beds will gradually become "raised beds" as you add improved soil each spring. This method reduces or eliminates rototilling, and so improves soil by not disturbing it.

Growing areas that are 30 inches wide work well because they accommodate plants of different sizes: Tomato or cabbage plants fit well in a single row, or you can plant two rows of medium-sized plants, like beans. Finally, this space is perfect for three rows of smaller plants like onions or beets.

Reduce the need to weed by growing plants continually throughout the summer. This means planting another crop when you harvest one. It can also mean planting "green manure" like red clover. Clover smothers weeds and adds nitrogen to your soil, and the red variety quickly decomposes.

Buckwheat is one of my favorite "smother crops." It goes from seed to flower in 30 days and provides nectar for bees while keeping the bed weed-free. I even plant turnips and kale seeds with buckwheat so the weeding is done for me! It also decomposes quickly, so I don't bother removing it from the garden.

Can you picture your garden now? Permanent paths lessen your work and allow you to walk comfortably without compressing the plants' growing space. Be imaginative when laying out the paths and beds. Your garden doesn't have to be a rectangle—a circle, triangle, square or elongated garden may be fun and attractive in your yard.

For those with no garden space: We who have garden space are fortunate, whether it be a patio container or a half acre. There are many people who would like to raise some of their own food but have no growing space. They may want access to healthier food, or they may need more affordable food during these tough economic times. What can we do to help?

There are many who are already helping with food pantries. This takes an immense amount of work and dedication and speaks to what wonderful people we have in our communities.

Could we also enable those without land to grow their own food? Europeans do this by renting space in shared garden areas. We could do this even in urban areas by converting unused lots or lawns into raised-bed gardens. The "square-foot gardening" technique works well for this because these gardens can be put on asphalt or grass, and they're inexpensive to set up and easy to maintain.

Common garden space might include people with gardening experience helping beginners. Others might donate their labor, and still others may donate part of their lawns. Some churches, schools and municipalities have lawns that take money, gasoline and sometimes toxic chemicals to maintain. What if some of this grass is converted to gardens? This proverb seems to apply: *Give a man a fish; feed him for a day. Teach a man to fish; feed him for a lifetime.* Artists and carpenters could add benches, arbors and art to create a park-like setting!

I've been told that growing food only applies to a small percent of people who enjoy gardening. I disagree. Our current food system cannot last forever, because it depends on three very fragile items: Cheap oil, plentiful water and a stable climate. If we are not growing local food for our own benefit, then we are learning these skills for our children. How wonderful if we build community at the same time.

→→ 7 ←←

Compost Is
Black Gold

Most land has lost its topsoil, so replacing it with compost is essential to raising good food. It will take years to fully rebuild your garden's topsoil, but as you annually add compost, you will be creating a soil that allows you to immediately grow better food. Your composting efforts are rewarded with produce that is incredibly flavorful. Additionally, your body directly benefits from eating this healthier food.

It's impossible to grow great-tasting produce without good soil. No matter the size of a garden, it's a big advantage to make your own compost. Compost is black, earthy-smelling, friable soil. It is what you "top-dress" your garden with each spring. It is as precious as "black gold" for growing healthy produce.

By definition, compost is organic material that has been broken down when exposed to air. If the compost is made from a great variety of materials, it has many nutrients. This type of soil is the secret to growing nutritious and delicious food.

Making compost isn't difficult, but I find all the information about it overwhelming. In reality, it's nature that does the composting and we only intervene to speed up the process. Here is a brief

These compost piles in the meadow are in various stages of decomposition. It will take about two more years for the closest pile pictured to become dark soil. During these two years, the pile will need moisture and turning for aeration.

outline on composting to get you started. You'll have no difficulty finding additional information from books and the web.

Compost ingredients: "Two parts brown to one part green" is the basic compost recipe. "Browns" include dry materials such as leaves, pine needles and dead plants. "Greens" usually are wetter materials like grass clippings and kitchen wastes.

Truthfully, I'm pretty bad at following any recipe, whether in the kitchen or when making compost. I figure Mother Nature doesn't always have the exact ingredients any more than I do! Therefore, I don't fret when dried leaves overwhelm other ingredients in the autumn. I add kitchen scraps and old plants from the garden, when they're available, and trust nature to take care of the rest.

Whether in forests or prairies, nature always incorporates animals' manure into her soil. When we do the same, we can have superior compost. If there's no possibility for chickens, rabbits or cows in your backyard, then see if you can find a farmer who has some extra manure to share.

Here are some hints about other ingredients I find helpful: *Never* use grass clippings that have been sprayed with chemicals. Shred leaves up with a lawn mower so they'll break down faster. Keep a "compost bucket" close to the kitchen sink to receive coffee grinds, eggshells, soiled paper towels, all vegetable peels and food wastes. Add leaves from deep-rooted plants like comfrey and trees to add more minerals. Include the soil clinging to plant roots when cleaning out the garden in the autumn. This soil has important living organisms that will multiply and help to break down and then rebuild the composting ingredients.

Compost containers: If you'll be working with a small amount of compost in the backyard, it may be worth investing in a compost container. The "tumbler composter" is convenient, and although relatively expensive, it will last for years. Alternatively, it's less expensive to use a couple backyard bins in which you turn the materials from one bin to the other.

Compliments of our farm animals, we have a lot of manure and straw. This results in several piles of compost out in the pasture. Commercial composting may be done on a cement base, but the organisms in the ground actually help provide the bacteria, fungi and earthworms that will help with decomposition.

Turning compost: The composting process requires oxygen, and turning compost helps all the material get oxygenated. The tumbler container is turned with a crank. Backyard piles are turned with a pitchfork to the adjacent site. To maximize the speed of composting, turn the compost every seven to ten days.

If you lose interest in turning it, it will still compost, but much more slowly. It may take three to eight *months* rather than four to eight *weeks*.

When the composting material is exposed to air, it heats up. You may even notice steam coming off it on a cool day. Because this heat kills weed seeds, it's very helpful to compost manure before it's used in your garden.

Moisture: Compost requires moisture, but not too much. Judge how your pile is doing by its smell. If you don't get the desired "earthy smell" when turning compost, it's probably too dry. To provide water, you can weave a soaker hose through the pile as you create it. You can also build the pile around a vertical drainage tile that provides air and can also be used for water.

If your pile smells bad, it may be too moist. The addition of straw or dried leaves will solve the problem. Unpleasant odors can also be caused by the material itself. Bury your kitchen wastes a few inches so they won't smell as they decompose.

Vermicomposting: This is a fancy term for having worms do the composting work for you. It is done in an indoor container which you can buy or build.

Building one sounds simple. Drill holes in the bottom of an 18-gallon plastic storage bin and place plastic mesh over the holes. Place the container on wooden blocks in an eight-inch tall, 30-quart plastic storage bin. The upper bin holds damp, shredded newspaper, a thin layer of soil, worms and kitchen scraps.

In return, the bottom bin gives you "worm tea," for fertilizer. The top container provides worm castings for excellent soil—and even extra worms for fishing!

Commercial compost: Producing food locally can contribute to the local economy in many ways. Imagine local farmers getting paid to keep yard wastes and food scraps out of the landfill. The addition of manure and aeration would result in excellent compost that could be sold back to us. The "wastes" become assets rather than pollutants and farmers get additional income. Local solutions are often win-win solutions.

Having backyard compost piles, or perhaps one per neighborhood, could reduce the amount of material going into landfills. Growing food in this compost would increase its flavor and nutrition. Composting may seem like a bother at first, but the truth is it may not be worth the bother to garden if we don't have this excellent soil for our plants.

8

Planting
Seeds Indoors

❝ Starting seeds indoors for your garden is fun. It's a chance to "play" in the soil and observe the plants more carefully than when they're outdoors. It's also a good excuse for getting a jump on warmer-weather projects. Don't worry about doing things "perfectly." The plants will show you what they need, and each following year will be easier. ❞

You will want to start some of your garden plants from seeds. This allows you to choose from a wider variety of crops than if you buy the plants. It is also more economical to start from seed. The biggest reason, however, is that starting from seed allows you to get your hands in soil while it's still cold outside!

The majority of seeds need about six weeks of growth before they're ready to be transplanted outdoors. To see when you can begin planting inside, find out the expected date of the last frost in your area and count back six weeks. Because the last frost in central Ohio is about mid-May, we begin the majority of our seeds the end of March.

I begin by gathering the variety of containers that have accumulated through the years. I start the seeds in 12-by-22-inch flats, but will transplant them into four-, six-, or eight-cell packs saved from previous nursery purchases. Yogurt or cottage cheese

These seedlings have already been transplanted from their original flats to individual containers. In addition to sunlight and moisture, they require air movement to prevent "damping-off."

containers work fine for transplants too, but all containers will need drainage. It's also helpful to have nonporous trays underneath containers to collect excess water.

The soil I use is a "seedling-starter planting media." I use it because it's sterile, and I don't want to introduce any diseases. Also, seeds don't need any nutrients at first. They're self-contained little miracles with all the nutrients they need to get started.

Before planting, the soil should be moist, but not soggy. It'll need repeated moistening with warm water to gradually permeate the soil.

The seeds I'll be starting are tomatoes, peppers, herbs, flowers and brassicas, like cauliflower and broccoli. Other seed packages say "direct-seed," and they will be planted right in the garden in warmer weather.

Space the seeds so they won't be overcrowded. In general, place fine seeds 1/8" apart, medium seeds ½" apart and large seeds 1" apart.

If the seed package says the seeds need light to germinate, then don't cover them. Otherwise, cover them completely with soil, but only to a depth of about four times the seeds' diameter. Sometimes it works well to lay seeds on the surface and push them gently down with a toothpick.

Cover your seed containers with saran wrap or clear plastic covers to keep the seeds moist.

Seeds actually need higher temperatures to germinate than what seedlings (baby plants) need. A south-facing window will do the trick, even though they might prefer a more constant temperature. Heating pads called "propagation mats" or soil cables keep temperatures more constant at 70 to 75 degrees, but both require electricity.

As soon as several seedlings appear, remove their covers. It's imperative for these tiny seedlings to have good air circulation.

It's also critical to keep the seeds and little plants moist, but not sopping wet. A spray bottle works well for watering, but you can also set the containers in warm water. Be extra careful on sunny afternoons that they don't entirely dry out.

Damping-off is a condition caused by a fungus. It's the main disease that can affect tiny seedlings. The seedlings fall over, their stems look pinched, and they die. Poor ventilation and overwatering are the culprits, and prevention is the only way to manage it.

To prevent damping-off, use only sterile soil medium for germination. From the start, provide good ventilation and avoid overwatering. When seedlings emerge, you can place sphagnum moss around them to inhibit fungal growth. Thin the plants to avoid overcrowding. When transplanting the seedlings to their individual containers, place the soil high in each pot so air can circulate around the stems.

Your seedlings' first leaves are called "seed leaves," and will not look like the plants' real leaves. Wait to thin and transplant your seedlings until they have their real leaves.

To thin the plants, don't pull up the unwanted seedlings. This will disturb the soil. Instead, use a tiny scissors to snip off the extra plants.

When transplanting to individual pots, use a very small spoon or a popsicle stick to keep as much soil around the roots as possible. Handle the plants by a leaf rather than a stem. The plant can always grow another leaf if you damage one.

Premoisten the soil in the plants' new containers, because this wet soil will settle. Seedlings can be planted a bit deeper in their new pots, so keep the soil high enough to give the plants good ventilation.

When the seedlings get their secondary leaves, they'll need additional nutrients to what they've been providing themselves. Use half-strength liquid fertilizer about every ten days.

After nurturing your plants so carefully, you want to make sure they make a safe transition to the outdoors. Plants started indoors are delicate and won't tolerate the sun and wind if planted directly into your garden. By early May in Ohio, when night temperatures are at least in the mid-50s, you can start putting them outdoors. Choose a sheltered place at first and take several days to gradually expose them to more sun and stronger breezes.

Each springtime is a bit different. If mid-May still has cool nights or stiff breezes, wait longer to put your precious plants in the garden. Waiting a week or two may result in earlier crops than having your young plants stunted by cold nights or strong winds. An option to waiting is to provide a windbreak around each plant. To do this, some people buy "walls of water" and others cut the bottoms off of plastic milk cartons and anchor a jug around each plant.

Start only a few plants indoors your first year so you have room on a sunny windowsill for them and can give them the care they need. As your confidence and skills grow, you will want to increase the number of garden plants that you begin from seeds.

#1
Leaf Plants
Chard·
Lettuce·
Broccoli·
Cabbage·
Cauliflower·
Brussels sprouts·

#2
Cleaners
& Builders
·Corn
·Potatoes
·Beans
·Peas
·Spinach

#4
Fruiting Plants
Tomatoes·
Squash·
Cucumbers·
Melons·
Peppers·

#3
Root Crops
·Onions
·Carrots
·Radishes
·Beets
·Turnips

9

Planning Your Garden

Mapping out where crops will grow in your garden allows you to enjoy planning for the next growing season. More importantly, it allows you to rotate your crops in such a way as to maximize their productivity. Even if your garden is small, you want to give it every advantage. The food you produce will be served at your dining room table, and you'll delight in how much better tasting it is than grocery store produce.

We have all winter to decide how to arrange plants in our garden. Where we put them does make a difference—not only for the present year, but for all the following years. So, let's get out both a blank sheet of paper and a list of what we're going to plant. It's time to map out what goes where.

There's one basic rule in planting your garden from year to year; don't plant the same thing in the same place two years in a row. This simple rule is the basis of crop rotation, and it's important for several reasons.

One reason for rotating crops is to reduce disease in your garden. Another is to reduce insect damage. Rotation also makes it easier to control weeds. Finally, crop rotation allows plants to benefit from how the previous year's crop enriched

This photo represents a garden plan that groups plants with similar needs together. Shown here are Red Perfection cabbage, Red Pontiac and Gold Yukon potatoes, Early Wonder Tall Top beets and Heinz tomatoes. After dividing your garden in four sections, you can rotate your crops each year as diagrammed here. Rotating crops in this order helps give the plants what they need from the soil, and helps prevent diseases from building up in the soil.

the soil. In other words, crop rotation increases the quality and quantity of your produce and decreases your work.

Each crop has particular diseases and pests that are attracted to it. These will build up in the soil if the same plants are grown there each year. The result is a steady decline in how much plants produce. Conventional farmers respond to this by spraying poisons on their plants. We can avoid poisons and keep crop production high by changing the location of our plants each year.

Rotating crops also helps to keep weeds from becoming established. Different crops have different depths to their roots and require different types of tillage. Weeds can't get established as easily when crops are rotated. Our other big secret to not having many weeds is the continual improvement of our soil. Weeds are often a sign of nutrient imbalance and nutrient depletion in the soil—but that is another chapter!

Another big reason for rotating crops is to balance their nutrient demands. Some groups of plants need high nitrogen in the soil, while others donate nitrogen. Other groups need potassium, while others crave phosphorus. Plants can be rotated to an area each year where they are assisted by what grew there the previous year. The sequencing of crop rotation is designed with that in mind.

Sound complicated? Well, I thought it was until I began keeping a "garden journal" from year to year. I have a three-hole punch, and so I use a three-ring binder that also holds other information about plants. A spiral-bound notebook would also work. It's helpful to keep notes throughout the summer of what crops you particularly like or what you intend to do differently the following year. Although it seems I would never forget, many details escape me by the next planting season.

Open a sheet of your journal now, label it for this year, and prepare your garden layout. I have finally devised a four-year crop rotation plan that continues to make sense to me from year to year. It takes into account the preventive measures mentioned above, as well as a plant's particular nutritional needs.

First divide the page into four parts. This means your garden will also need dividing into four sections. When spring weather tempts you back outside, you can set up the growing areas and the walking paths. For the planning stage, divide the page in four parts and label each quadrant as the paragraphs are labeled below. Then write the names of plants that belong in each quadrant for reference when you plant. Ready?

#1 Leaf plants (need high nitrogen/compost): Lettuce, salad greens, spinach, broccoli, brussels sprouts, cabbage, cauliflower, kale, kohlrabi.

#2 Cleaners and Builders: Corn, potatoes (both considered "cleaners"), beans, peas (considered "builders" because they increase nitrogen in soil).

#3 Root plants (need high potassium): Onions, shallots, garlic, scallions, leeks, carrots, beets, turnips, radishes.

#4 Fruiting plants (need high phosphorus): Squash, cucumbers, melons, pumpkins, tomatoes, peppers, eggplants.

Next, draw arrows (in contrasting ink for fun) to show which direction these quadrants will "turn" the next year. Number one needs the most nitrogen, so it follows number two which contributes nitrogen. Each quadrant rotates up one number each year. I divided our garden into four quadrants, so I rotate the crops in a clockwise motion each year. Rotation can also be done in four linear sets of rows where crops are planted one section over each year. If I'm making this sound difficult, it's because my brain has trouble with this, and I have to rely on my "map" from the previous year!

There's another difficulty with crop rotation; all quadrants don't take the same amount of space. For example, corn never fits where the little root crops did. My answer to that is to go back to the simplest rule—don't plant the same thing in the same place two years in a row. It'll fit *somewhere*—just don't plant it where it was the previous year. And having the garden journal insures that I know where things were the previous year.

Companion planting (see chapter ten) also offers a challenge because good companions aren't always in the same quadrant. That's not a big problem if we've kept track of what we planted where. The more creative and experimental methods we try, the more fun we'll have.

Gardening is fun if you have a sense of adventure, a willingness to learn and more than a little humor. Enjoy personalizing your journal and your journey.

➤➤ 10 ◄◄

Growing Food without Chemicals

"When we work with nature, it helps us grow beautiful and nutritious food. We "battle" nature when we use chemicals to kill insects and weeds. This is a battle that we can never win. Nature continues to build defenses as we spend our money buying ever more toxic chemicals. Let's choose instead to have nature as our ally. The result is a garden that nurtures us with poison-free food and with beauty. It also becomes a safe place for all of nature's creatures."

There are many reasons that people have gardens and raise their own food: it's fun to have our hands in the soil, growing food is cheaper than going to the store, and homegrown food is both more flavorful and more nutritious than commercially grown food. Another big reason we grow our own produce is to avoid the chemicals that are ubiquitous in most grocery store produce.

To avoid poisons in our gardens and raise healthy crops, we must learn the tricks of growing fruits and vegetables without the ease of zapping the bad bugs with chemicals. I've tried a variety of techniques over the years, and would like to share some of the methods I find best in preventing insect damage.

1. Insects go after the weakest plants, so

The row cover shown here is being used over squash to prevent the "vine borer" moth from laying eggs on the vines. The moth's larvae and pupae kill the plants of cucumbers, gourds, melons, pumpkins and squash before their fruits can ripen. Using a row cover, however, means the cover has to be intermittently removed for weeding and hand-pollinating.

healthy plants are the best defense against insect damage. I can't stress enough that the secret of having healthy plants is having great soil. First, remember to compost! Dress your beds and plants with compost at least annually. Just as eating nutritious food is necessary for a strong immune system, plants need good nutrition from the soil to stay healthy. See "Compost Is Black Gold" *(chapter 7)*.

A second way to continually improve your soil is to plant legumes. This will be part of your garden rotation (see "Planning Your Garden"), but you can also plant legumes whenever you get an open spot in your garden. Legumes "smother" weeds and also build the nitrogen content of the soil.

2. A change in our attitude can be a big help in reducing the amount of chemicals we use. A commercial apple has over twenty chemicals sprayed on it during its growth. Learning to tolerate some imperfections, like superficial brown spots, will help you avoid many of these chemicals. Likewise, don't let a grasshopper's nibble on the celery or a "parsley worm's" munching on your parsley make you use chemicals. Tolerate the nibble, and rejoice that the parsley worm will turn into a black swallowtail butterfly! In other words, live with a few blemishes rather than use poisons.

3. Don't let diseases build up in your garden by growing crops in the same location they grew in the previous year or two. It's essential to rotate your crops each year. See "Planning Your Garden" *(chapter 9)*.

4. Rather than chemicals, use barriers to keep harmful insects from your plants. Row covers can exclude vine borers from your cucumbers or pumpkins. These covers are temporarily removed to weed and to allow pollination, and then replaced over the plants. Cutworms can be kept from your seedlings by placing a barrier around their stems at planting time. I use drainage tile for these barriers, which I cut into sections about four inches in length with a drywall knife. Finally, for precious fruit growing on trees, I place a footie (found in shoe stores) on each fruit when it is very small. The footie expands as the apple or peach grows, and protects it from predators.

5. Plant resistant varieties of fruits and vegetables. It's true that I prize old breeds of plants because I think it's important to save their genetics.

However, if I don't want to use chemicals, I find it helpful sometimes to use hybrids. The only reason I can raise flawless cabbage is because I use a hybrid variety of seed. That means I can't save seeds to plant next year, but for now I enjoy the ease of using hybrids for this one category of plant.

6. Don't categorize all insects as "bad." As I mentioned, the little fellow munching on your parsley has the potential to become a butterfly. Other beneficial insects should be welcomed to keep down the number of pests. Many beetles, not just ladybugs, are important in keeping the pests at bay. Get to know and protect the insects that are assisting you.

7. Besides welcoming beneficial insects, some plants can also help prevent insect damage. "Companion planting" will help protect your produce. Marigolds can be planted not only between tomato plants, but throughout your garden. Mint deters cabbage moths and nasturtiums discourage squash bugs and aphids. Buckwheat attracts beneficial insects while it feeds the bees and provides green manure. As you add "companion plants" to help protect your produce, you will also be benefiting helpful insects by adding diversity.

8. Create an environment where birds and other beneficial insects will come to your aid. The harmful insects love sun, so nurture shady, covered areas for the good guys like beetles. Droopy cosmos plants and straw mulch are examples of providing protected areas. The more complex your garden is, the better your garden environment is for helpful wildlife. Allow berries to grow on fences and have an arbor or tepee for vine plants. Living barriers along fences can actually prevent flying insects from entering your garden in large numbers. Vary the height of your plants. You might want to alternate bush beans with climbing beans, or place a row of cabbage between the rows of tomatoes.

As your garden becomes more complex, it becomes a welcoming place for beneficial insects. At the same time, you might find that you also enjoy spending more time in the beautiful habitat that is your garden.

➤➤ 11 ⤙⤙

Local Food Includes
Local Animals

❝ When we raise our own meat, eggs or milk, we are rewarded with delicious food. Allowing animals to be outdoors in the sunshine, eating grass, results in food that is more flavorful than you can ever purchase in the store. It's also reassuring to know that this food is much better for your health than food raised commercially. Additionally, your entire family can enjoy caring for these beautiful animals. ❞

In previous chapters, we discussed raising our own crops because we want healthier food and a healthier environment. Now that we've got the basics down for gardening, let's talk about animals, our other important source of food.

All over the world, animals provide humans with meat, a basic source of protein. Even in poor or urban areas, people find room for chickens, rabbits and even guinea pigs. Okay, I admit that those last two seem more like pets to me, but I suspect I could change that view if I got hungry enough and didn't have anything else to eat.

I've already learned to eat meat from animals I've known. After we bought our little farm and began repairing the outbuildings, we bought baby chickens. Because neither my husband nor I grew up on farms, even these critters were quite

These are juvenile Narragansett turkeys. This rare heirloom breed dates back to the 17th century when the European domestic turkey was crossed with the eastern wild turkey. They were valued for their superior-flavored meat and the fact that they are such excellent foragers that they require little supplemental feed. The American Livestock Breeds Conservancy now lists the Narragansett turkeys as "threatened," which means there are fewer than 1,000 breeding birds in the United States.

a challenge to raise and to eat. We're pretty amazed that they've come to provide such an abundance of both eggs and meat. Maybe what surprises us most, however, is how much we enjoy their company. Their antics provide plenty of backyard entertainment.

We were grateful to have the help of a friend the first time we killed chickens. He had a balance of reverence and humor that we continue to rely on when doing this task. Because half of all offspring are male, eating chickens is the only way not to have a backyard full of fighting roosters. The task seems especially worthwhile now that we've learned that backyard chickens are much more nutritious and tastier than chicken meat from the store.

We next bought two cows. We wanted to make better use of the meadow and thought it would be fun to have some milk. We didn't realize how generous nature is, and we have had an abundance of meat and milk since that time. We also have an abundance of *manure*, and thus compost for the garden.

A pair of pigs was next in line, and then some beehives. Most recently, heritage turkeys have joined the menagerie. Because we haven't done any of this before, it's all been accompanied by lots of book learning and help from friends, as well as many mistakes and much laughter. Our reward is the healthiest and best-tasting food that we have had in our lives. We also live a rich life filled with beautiful creatures.

Let's back up a bit and look at how important it is to have animals in order to farm in a "sustainable" manner. The word "sustainable" has become fashionable in the last few years, just as "organic" now sounds familiar. I define sustainable as the ability to grow both our own food and the food for our animals without going outside the farm or the community for what is needed. It also means that our farm doesn't create excess manure that could contaminate groundwater. Instead, manure and straw bedding are composted into soil to feed our garden.

Sustainability also means not continually buying inputs for the farm. It should be able to "sustain" itself. We have become pretty independent of the grocery store, but at this stage, we still have a grocery bill for some of the animals' food. We're fortunate to be able to buy what our animals need from within our community.

Sustainability could also be defined as preserving farmland for future generations. What we want is to "sustain" good soil, a water supply and genetics for future years and for future generations.

Animals are important, because they provide the manure that keeps soil fertile—whether it's in the meadow or in compost. I know of a vegetable farmer who has cows only because he needs good compost for raising his crops. If we want good food, we need animals. Agriculture in the United States has eroded topsoil ten times faster than it can be replaced. When we use animals to create compost for topsoil, we are planning for the future.

Besides having animals for healthy food and soil, we've chosen rare breeds to help save their genetics. I stressed the importance of preserving genetics when talking about seeds. Genetic preservation is also important for many old breeds of farm animals. They are threatened with extinction because corporate farming, which produces most of our food, uses uniform-sized, high-production, hybrid animals. Therefore, the more variety of plant and animal genetics we can help save, the more likely our grandchildren will be able to grow their own food. The more of us that have a few "rare breeds" in our backyards, the more rare breeds will survive.

I encourage you to get information from the American Livestock Breeds Conservancy (ALBC). You might be alarmed to see how many animals are close to extinction, but it's also fun to read about their history and look at their photos. ALBC has a network of members who exchange ideas and animals. Some may only have a few chickens or a couple cows, but it's thrilling to help preserve genetics that served our ancestors so well. By choosing from these breeds, we also end up with hardier animals which serve us well.

In the next few chapters, I'll discuss what it takes to keep animals for either meat or their produce—eggs or milk. You can share in this good food by having animals yourselves. You can also buy from local farmers, and support the economic health of your community. Eating local food makes for healthier individuals, community and environment.

⇁⇥ 12 ⇤↽

Backyard Chickens May Be for You

Most of us don't hesitate to take responsibility for a house pet like a dog, and yet might feel that caring for chickens is too difficult. What's amazing about chickens, however, is that they don't require much daily attention. They won't need a walk when you come home from work, but they'll keep you entertained when you sit on the back steps. You'll be their hero if you feed them table scraps, and they'll reward you with their content clucking and fresh eggs. When you think about it, chickens may be the ideal pets!

I'd like to begin talking about animals by discussing chickens—just because they're so much fun. Besides enjoyment, there are plenty of practical reasons to have them: It doesn't take much land to produce both meat and eggs. It gives you and your children a "farm" experience without a huge investment. They can be easier to care for than a dog. Chickens are entertaining and make good pets. You can enjoy their eggs without having a noisy rooster. Finally, the eggs and meat you get from your own chickens are far healthier than what you get from the store.

We began having chickens about seven years ago, after refurbishing an old chicken house. I wanted an old breed of chickens so we could help save their genetics, so I looked at the American

This portable chicken coop is called a "chicken tractor." It can be moved once or twice a day to provide fresh forage for the chickens. Chicken manure is acidic, so sprinkling lime on the grass after each move will keep your lawn beautiful.

Livestock Breeds Conservancy's poultry list. I saw Dorking chickens listed on their "critical" list, and chose them because they are good for both eggs and meat.

Years ago we attempted raising chickens at a friend's farm. We were told to get "Cornish-cross" birds that are a hybrid raised for meat. On the positive side, I have to admit that after six to eight weeks, the birds were large enough to put in the freezer. That's economical. On the downside, we were shocked to see them with broken legs and congestive heart failure because of their large breasts. The Cornish-cross is what you buy as chicken meat in the store, but they sure don't make an attractive backyard flock. We're sticking with heritage breeds because they are "sustainable." However, if I wanted to produce lots of meat to sell I would buy Cornish-cross chickens. If I wanted to sell lots of eggs, I would buy a "layer" like the Leghorn chicken.

Because Dorking chickens are rare, we had to originally order baby chicks through the mail from hatcheries. Since that time, we keep a rooster so that we can hatch out our own babies. This makes a heritage breed chicken most economical.

However, our chickens don't mature until about 20 to 22 weeks of age. That's when most the boys (cockerels) go in the freezer and the girls (pullets) start laying eggs. Our chickens cost more to raise than hybrids because they grow more slowly, but they now give us wonderful eggs because they have the ability to free-range. The cockerels give high-quality meat because they do mature more slowly and their protein is more complex than fast-growing hybrids. When the hens get old, they sometimes go in the freezer too. But *that* depends on how fond we've grown of them!

Hens will lay eggs without a rooster, but we keep a rooster so we can have fertilized eggs for hatching. One rooster works out well for 10 to 15 hens, and even makes a good pet. You may have to live in the country to have a rooster though—not everyone appreciates being notified when the day begins!

Many towns and cities are changing their ordinances to allow hens in backyards to make local food more available. Sometimes it's the local government that takes leadership to encourage community gardens and chickens in order to have more "food security." Often it's individuals who help change ordinances to allow small livestock in town because they're concerned about the price, quality or safety of their food.

To get the full health benefits of raising your own chickens, it's important that they can forage outside. This is not just kinder than having them spend their lives in cages—they also produce much healthier eggs and meat. Their meat has "good" types of cholesterol and omega-3s when they have foraged on grass.

In comparison to factory farms, eggs of free-range chickens have:

⅓ less cholesterol
¼ less saturated fat
⅔ more vitamin A
Twice as much omega-3 fatty acids

Three times as much vitamin E
Three to six times more vitamin D
Seven times more beta carotene

What was humbly known as backyard chickens are now called "free-range" chickens, and their eggs can sell for over four dollars a dozen. You'll want some of those in *your* backyard!

Before you begin with chickens, I suggest getting a basic book on backyard chickens. I still use mine as a reference when I have questions, so it's been worth the relatively small investment. Basic reading will help you give the babies a good start and assist you in housing and feeding your chickens. It's also helpful to understand their peculiarities like molting, reduced laying in winter and broodiness.

Chickens are perfect for even urban backyards, because they can be housed in small coops. A chicken lays an egg every day or two, so having four chickens will mean having fresh, healthy eggs every day. These eggs will have bright yellow yolks, firm whites and a great taste. They'll make your chicken project well worthwhile.

Starting with four or five hens means you can build or buy a small coop, and there are many to choose from. Some homemade models which can be moved around the yard are called "chicken tractors." These insure that the chickens have plenty of fresh grass and insects to choose from, while being protected from predators. Allowing them to forage on pasture or grass keeps them healthy and their eggs healthful.

Even a small coop will allow you to close them safely in at night, and that's when they're in the most peril from predators. Fortunately, it's not necessary to round up your chickens each evening. It's natural for them to go inside to their roosts at dusk. You then just securely close their doors and say *good-night!*

⤚ 13 ⤙

Keeping Heritage Breed Cows

What a thrill to enjoy all the benefits of old breeds while helping to save these precious genetics for the future. Raising milk animals is so much easier when we do it the way nature intended—avoiding hormones that force them to produce more milk, and allowing them to be out in the sunshine on pasture. When animals live as nature intended, they stay healthy and we benefit from their nutritious milk and meat. We also hope their descendants will be there to help our descendants survive.

We bought two cows, not because we knew anything about them, but because we had a pasture and a barn. Homesteading and heritage breed cattle seem to complement each other, so we looked at American Livestock Breeds Conservancy (ALBC) to see what rare breeds were listed. We chose Dutch Belted because they are on the "critical" list, and are good for both milk and meat, and also because their Oreo-cookie appearance is beautiful.

In the dairy world today, *Holstein* cows have become almost synonymous with *dairy* cows. Over the past 40 years, they have been bred to double their milk supply while losing other beneficial traits. Likewise, it's now assumed that beef cattle need to be confined and fed grain

These Dutch Belted cows are a dual-purpose breed that provides both milk and meat. The American Livestock Breeds Conservancy lists them as "critical" because their estimated global population is less than 2,000. Our cows stay with their young and are entirely grass-fed.

to produce good beef. It's now known that confinement beef not only produces unhealthy fats to eat, but confinement of a large number of animals in one place contaminates our environment. We're fortunate to live in a rural area where we have the option to return to healthy ways to raise cows—healthy for humans, the cows and the environment. This takes "old-time" genetics. Let me explain:

Dutch Belted cows live to be about 20 years old, and they calve annually from age two through their teens. This is an incredible difference from today's confinement dairy cow whose average lifespan is just over three years. The sisters we originally bought, Addie and Annie, are now seven and eight years old and should be with us for another twelve years!

It's fortunate for us, who knew nothing about cows, that old-breed cows don't have many birthing problems. We knew no better than to be totally delighted to watch them while they had their babies. This is the norm with heritage cows.

The Dutch Belted's excellent health is another thing I have taken for granted. To avoid mastitis, we do have to milk routinely after they give birth. They produce far more milk than one calf can handle for the first three to four months. After that we milk when we want to (because the calves take the rest)—after all, we're a homestead and not a dairy.

The calves have also been problem-free, but because the calves nurse from their mothers it's easy to avoid health problems like scours. However, Dutch Belted also demonstrate good health at dairies where cows and calves must be separated.

These cows are known for their good dispositions. Now, I've never dealt with an ornery cow, but I've heard that they can be mean. Instead, we compare our cows to the horses, and therefore appreciate the cows' incredible patience. We also find them easy to work into new routines and enjoy their trust and response to kindness.

We appreciate our cows' economical size. Dry years have made both pasture and hay precious commodities. Our cows' smaller size is important so that we don't have to feed more in order to have them remain healthy. They eat only grass or hay and we receive excellent milk and meat.

One may assume that a cow knows how to graze, and indeed, heritage cattle wouldn't have survived otherwise. Many modern confinement cows have lost the ability to graze. By having our cows go to the grass rather than having the grass brought to them, our work and expenses are reduced.

We didn't understand at first that these cows would mean such an abundance of excellent food for us. How wonderful it is to have raw milk without antibiotics or hormones. This allows us to have cheese, yogurt, butter and ice cream of the same excellent quality. The steers are slaughtered at nine months (a natural time for the mothers to wean them), and this becomes our grass- and milk-fed "baby beef." This meat is incredibly tender and flavorful. Studies show that grass-fed beef is much healthier to eat than meat that comes from confinement lots.

People express surprise that we treat our animals with such affection and respect and yet eat the males, but we have come to understand that the breed will not be saved unless they are eaten. This dichotomy is understood when you see a pasture filled with steers that are "pets" but leave no genetics for the future. Today, there are only about 200 Dutch Belted cows of breeding age in the United States. We hope to leave behind a few more for the next generations.

The above characteristics combine to make heritage breed cows economical to keep. Even though they don't produce the Holstein's quantity of milk, we save money because there are fewer vet bills, we feed no grain, the cows calve annually, and they live long. These benefits prove important not only for the homesteader, but for grazing dairies that are "breeding up" their herd to be Dutch Belted.

We came to understand the breeding-up program when we originally tried to buy the rare Dutch Belted cows. To bring them back from close-to-extinction, this program allows milk cows to be crossed with full-blooded Dutch Belted bulls. Every female offspring is registered, and the fifth generation (F-5) is 96.88% Dutch Belted and registered as full-blooded. Although we haven't gotten there yet, we are enjoying all the benefits of having an old-time breed.

We wanted a couple cows for milk and meat, and now we're talking about helping to save a rare breed. How did this happen? I guess we fell in love with these sweet and beautiful animals and would like to leave a few more behind to help both cows and people survive. How fortunate for us that they also give us such highly nutritious and delicious food.

➤➤ 14 ◄◄

Fresh Milk Is a Nutritious Food

"Having dairy animals is a big step towards food security. Milk is a "whole food" that contains proteins, fats and carbohydrates. When animals are grass-fed, this food contains only the "good" fats, and plenty of vitamins and minerals. Having fresh milk allows you to create cheeses, yogurt and butter. These animals also contribute to the compost pile, which becomes your garden's soil. You'll get the bonus of growing highly nutritious vegetables!"

It's fun to have our own milk, but you don't have to have cows to do this. Even two acres are enough for a couple milk goats that can provide you with milk and wonderful cheese. The only problem is that animals don't have an "on-off" switch. When they have their babies and the milk arrives, the amount can seem overwhelming. Perhaps the ideal situation would be to have dairy animals for each neighborhood so both the milk and the chores could be shared. Here is how we manage the milk on our homestead.

When our two Dutch Belted cows have their calves, they each give about five gallons of milk a day. Our home abounds in milk and cheese and other dairy products at this time, but we also have the work of the other farm animals, a large garden

The equipment in this photo is a cheese press and a butter churn. Beginning at 12 o'clock there is cheddar cheese (which has been dipped in red paraffin for aging), yogurt, butter, ice cream (with homegrown strawberries), Swiss cheese and fresh milk.

and other family chores. We're gradually learning how to weave the milk-processing chores into our busy schedule.

First of all, we try to stagger the cows' calving by two months so the peak quantities of milk don't coincide. The calves continue to nurse until nine months of age and by four or five months can consume all their mothers' milk. This still gives us at least six of the busiest months of the year to deal with surplus milk.

Step one is to drink all we can. Raw milk is more of a food than a beverage, and I love its complex and delicious flavor. Its natural bacteria are helpful "probiotics" for the gut. People with lactose intolerance can drink it because it contains the necessary enzymes. European studies show that children who drink it have less asthma. We drink it because it's available and tastes great!

The cows give far more milk than what we can drink, however, and when the first cow has her calf in April, the race begins. Yogurt is a daily staple at our house and is easy to make. I save about ½ cup of yogurt from the previous batch and mix it with a quart of milk right from the cow. This is kept at about 100 degrees F until the next morning when I wake up to fresh yogurt for breakfast. Yogurt makers can be either electric or insulated containers.

Making homemade cheese is as simple as separating curds from whey. The curds contain the solid protein and the whey has most of the lactose. Your "coagulating agent" will usually be vinegar or citric acid with soft cheeses like mozzarella or ricotta. Rennet is used in hard cheeses like cheddar. My big time-saver is to use the milk right after milking, when it's about 90 degrees F. This is the perfect temperature for separating curds and whey in soft cheeses and for adding a bacterial starter in hard cheeses. It's even the perfect temperature for yeast in bread making. I can't always begin cheese making right after milking, so I wrap a couple bath towels around the ten-liter milk container to maintain the milk's temperature until other chores are done.

My favorite homemade cheese recipe is mozzarella cheese because it's so fast. It takes one gallon of milk, citric acid and rennet, and only ½ hour with a microwave. The other soft cheese I make is ricotta. It can be made from one gallon of whey or whole milk plus citric acid. If hung in cheesecloth for a short time, it's moist and can be used as a dip for chips or vegetables. Hanging longer makes a drier, firmer cheese that is great for stir-fry or lasagna. Soft cheeses are bland, so flavor it with salt, garlic and herbs to fit your menu. These recipes and many of my supplies, instructions and equipment come from the New England Cheesemaking Supply Company.

Harder cheeses do take longer to make and require more equipment, like a thermometer and cheese press. I make a lot of cheddar cheese because it takes two gallons of milk to make when I want to use as much milk as possible. The first step in making cheddar is adding a bacterial starter. After 45 minutes, rennet is added to coagulate the milk. After this, the curds are put in a cheese press and then aged. This cheese is our milk product during the winter months when we don't milk.

Clabbered cheese is the easiest cheese to make because it makes itself. The milk directly from the cow is simply left to sit until its natural bacteria multiply enough to slightly acidify the milk. The milk then naturally separates into curds and whey in about two to three days, depending on its surrounding temperature. I hang the curds in cheesecloth until they're the consistency that I want. My mouth waters now to think of the wonderful flavor of this simple cheese.

Butter is made by saving the twice-a-day milk in the basement and "creaming it off" in the morning. I use a small cup to skim off the cream and put it in the "Daisy butter churn." Sitting in the 65-degree basement overnight allows the cream to slightly sour, and this gives the butter a delightful, full flavor. A by-product of making butter is buttermilk—and there's no better combination than homemade butter and buttermilk biscuits!

It's no wonder that milk is called the perfect food and that people all over the world depend on it. Having a source of real milk is a big step towards food independence.

⇢ 15 ⇠

Successful Beekeeping with Your Own Honeybees

❝ Beekeeping has brought me closer to nature. It has made me more aware of what these insects need and how complex their life is inside the hive. This awareness gives me the pleasure of cooperating with them in simple ways like allowing the basil and broccoli to flower, so I can watch and listen to them while weeding the garden. Being around them quiets my insides and makes my life richer. Honey and wax become a "bonus" above this pleasure. ❞

If you've thought about beekeeping, I strongly encourage you to begin. There are continually new things to learn, observe and enjoy. It brings you close to nature, and there's the bonus of well-pollinated crops and raw honey.

People tell me their yard is the size of a "postage stamp" so they don't have room for a garden. But a postage stamp is big enough for a hive of bees! The secret to having bees and having harmony with your neighbors is twofold. First, face the entrance to the beehive close to a high shrub or fence. The bees will climb high to exit and be over the heads of the neighbors when they go off to forage. Secondly, provide your bees with water so they don't congregate at your neighbors' swimming pools or

One frame of the top-bar hive is lifted to show the bees' natural comb. Many worker bees are caring for their brood. Some hexagon-shaped cells are filled with honey or pollen.

birdbaths.

When I began beekeeping, I didn't enjoy it as much as I do now. I followed most recommendations from books and classes, even if I was uncomfortable with them. In 2007, three-quarters of honeybees died in Ohio, whether or not people used chemicals in their hives. That made me more confident to trust my own instincts. The result is that I enjoy beekeeping much more and my beehives have grown from the original two to eight.

I do think that it's important to read, meet other beekeepers through your local bee association, listen to their speakers and even find a mentor for your first year. But I would encourage you to use your "common sense" and not feel compelled to use chemicals or artificial food supplements. The following strategies work for me and may help you enjoy beekeeping from the start.

Avoid chemicals: Mites are one reason that chemicals are routinely used in beehives. I stopped all chemicals after my first year, and now "treat" mites by dusting the bees with powdered sugar to help them groom off the mites. The bottoms of my hives are made out of screen so the mites will fall through. Honeybees continue to live with mites but gradually build sufficient resistance to stay healthy.

Bees forage over a two-mile radius, so it's difficult to protect them from all chemicals. Remind your neighbors that insecticides kill bees, which are necessary for pollination. It may help to bribe them with a jar of honey.

Provide a varied diet: Bees are used commercially today to pollinate just one crop, like almonds. Bees need variety to make their own foods from nectar and pollen, and to maintain a strong immune system. City dwellers have the advantage of many neighbors with flowers and gardens.

Bees need a healthful and varied diet, just as our bodies do. Keeping bees helps us be aware that all of nature is very interconnected. We make compost to feed the microbes in the soil. Our plants then become well-nourished and we get nutrient-dense food from our plants. We need the bees to pollinate our plants, and the pollen and nectar the bees gather sustain them, and help to nourish us.

Bees motivate me to keep planting. Our orchard has fruit trees, daffodils, white clover, comfrey and berries. Annual flowers fit in the vegetable garden, and I plant only sunflowers that have pollen. I rotate the garden plants around certain perennials that feed the bees, like herbs and bee balm.

Buckwheat is our autumn cover crop and its nectar is far superior to sugar water for the bees' winter food.

Don't be greedy: It sounds like common sense to allow the bees enough of their own honey and pollen to feed their young and stay healthy themselves. Many people take the honey and honeycomb for profit and expect the bees to live on sugar water or high fructose corn syrup. If you want healthy bees, allow them the fruits of their labor. Healthy bees will make enough honey for you too.

Buy new equipment but recycle bees: Used beehives and frames may easily harbor disease and chemicals. Buying new beekeeping supplies will assure a fresh start. Beginning bee supplies, including safety gear, cost about $220. The honey extractor costs around $300, but can be shared.

Buying the beehives makes beekeeping expensive. A less expensive alternative is a "top-bar hive" that you can build yourself. The directions can be found on the "Barefoot Beekeeper" site. It's a more natural way to keep bees, because they build their own comb. This means you can't extract the honey from the wax, but you can have "comb honey"—the type where honey is in the waxy comb. I think a top-bar hive is a very enjoyable way to observe the bees.

A package of bees with a queen bee costs about $80. I would much rather get my equipment and then ask another beekeeper to help me find a swarm. Besides saving money, a swarm consists of local bees that have their own queen and are healthy enough to have already multiplied. By using local bees, we don't risk importing diseases or Africanized bees.

Enjoy bee therapy: I feel good to contribute to the honeybees' health, and living with bees enhances my world. Despite my natural squeamishness with insects, I can become calm and centered when working around the hum of the honeybees.

I am also grateful for their beautiful raw honey. We use it often on our farm for its amazing ability to heal wounds. Not only does it have natural antibiotic qualities, but it contains hydrogen peroxide that keeps the wound clean. Bacteria are becoming resistant to many antibiotics, but raw honey keeps on healing.

Europe has done many studies on the medicinal qualities of eating raw, local honey. Its many benefits include helping the immune system, reducing allergies, providing antioxidants and helping digestion.

Whether you live in the country, suburbs or city, I think you'll find that life is definitely better when you can include bees in your life and treat them the way that nature intended.

⤞ 16 ⤝

Rainwater Harvesting

It's quite easy for us Midwesterners to take rain for granted—that is, until we get a dry year. When water does come down from the sky, it makes good sense to save some of it for a "dry day." We might be saving rainwater to help our garden along, but in doing so we are also saving water for future generations. The more of us that use water from rain barrels or cisterns, the more water will remain in underground aquifers. It also feels good to be more self-sufficient in a basic necessity like water.

When we talk about harvesting local food, we expect to talk about tomatoes or honey, and not rainwater. But it's easy to see that water is essential to our own existence and absolutely necessary to raise the food we eat. Although it is precious to all living things, water is one of our most wasted resources.

Collecting rainwater for our gardens can be helpful on many levels. Municipal water is treated, but only two percent of treated water is actually drunk. Putting city water on your garden not only puts chemicals on your plants, but it can make watering your garden quite expensive. Country folk get their water from wells, but pumping it increases their electric bills.

During times of heavy rains, municipal storm

This urban water-catchment system is usually filled with the spring's rain and then provides water for the backyard garden throughout the hot summer. It also helps to prevent the city's storm system from being overwhelmed in the wet season.

systems can become overloaded. Diverting some water to your garden will help the system work. The states of Washington and Oregon actually pay their citizens to harvest rainwater so it doesn't go into the municipal system. During the other extreme of drought, you can supplement the city's reservoir by using your personal supply of water.

Finally, using rainwater for your garden is the environmentally responsible thing to do. Using rainwater for our gardens helps conserve water for the future and assures us a supply in late summer when we need it.

In areas of the country that don't receive enough rain to keep the gardens growing, the soil may be of the type that water penetrates easily. Because rainwater is a salt-free source of clean water, harvesting it for garden watering will force salt that accumulates in the soil down beyond root growth. This allows roots to grow and take up water better and plants become more drought resistant.

What amazes me about saving rainwater is how much can be collected from a small roof. To calculate this, it's helpful to know that one square foot of collection area and one inch of rain will result in six-tenths of a gallon of rainwater. The part of Ohio I live in receives about 37 inches of rain a year. Therefore, a 750-square-foot roof can yield 16,650 gallons of water a year. Fortunately, you don't have to catch and store it all!

To begin, it helps to calculate how much water you want stored before your driest growing months. Gardens need about an inch of water a week. (Remember to mulch your garden well to help conserve the soil's moisture.) If you know your garden size, you can actually calculate how much water you need to store for these months. That will tell you what type of collection, storage and distribution systems you will need.

The horizontal surface that gets rained on is your *collection* system. The *storage* system can be either rain barrels or cisterns, depending on how much water you need. Rain barrels vary in cost from about $60 to $200. They average about 55 gallons in size, and should be "food-grade." Some come with a spout and hose and are made to be low maintenance. All rain barrels have covers that prevent mosquitoes from breeding. If you make your own, be sure to have it covered. In the fall, the barrels should be drained and cleaned out and the downspout reconnected.

Cisterns are used by people with larger gardens. They can be concrete or plastic. Some rain barrels and cisterns can be found on Craig's List. Some cities have businesses that set the system up for you.

Now that you have an idea about collecting and storing rainwater, you'll need a *distribution* system. Basically, you can choose between an active or a passive system depending on how big a system you have and how much money you want to put into it. Either system requires hoses, pipes or simply buckets.

A passive distribution system uses gravity and will take some patience to get the water from your source to the garden. If your collection barrel is up on cement blocks and has a hose that reaches to your garden, you have a complete system that will require more patience than energy. Some people connect soaker hoses directly to their rain barrels so that their gardens get additional water whenever it rains.

An active distribution system requires a power source. If you bury your cistern tank, you'll obviously need some muscle, electricity or wind power to pump the water back up above ground. If you want your water with more pressure behind it than gravity provides, you'll also need a power source such as an electrical pump.

There are books and web sites on rainwater harvesting. There are also businesses to help you set up a rainwater collection system. Saving rainwater this year may help your garden during a dry spell. It may also help our children and grandchildren have adequate water to survive.

17

Plant Perennials for Food

❝ Many of us have more ideas about what we would like to grow than we have time or energy. That is why planting perennials is so satisfying. It does take time and work to plant a fruit tree or berry bush, and it also takes attention to keep it watered until the roots are established. After that initial investment, however, perennials work for you. When you plant an apple tree no larger than a twig, imagine it as an old, gnarled tree still giving you apples in your old age! ❞

Many tasks like mowing grass, weeding the garden and doing dishes seem to get undone as quickly as we do them. Perhaps that's why I find getting food from perennial plants so satisfying. It takes some effort the first year to get them planted and growing, but then with a little encouragement they will provide food for years to come.

Entire books have been written about strawberries or fruit trees, but let's just do an overview of some perennial possibilities. This will give you an opportunity to decide what foods you would enjoy having in your own yard. You can also begin to imagine locations that would make good homes for them.

Rhubarb and asparagus are the first fresh

These strawberries are our first fruit in the spring. Because they're so plentiful at that time, I freeze some to eat later in the year. It's also possible to plant "everbearing" strawberries that will give less fruit at one time, but will bear fruit throughout the summer.

foods available in the spring at our house. Rhubarb is well suited for Ohio because it is a cool-season vegetable that requires winters below 40 degrees. It is best planted at the edge of the garden, though its large leaves are also suitable for a perennial garden bed. It thrives in well-drained, organic soil, and our rhubarb flourishes with an extra helping of compost in the fall. Because I like its sour taste, the first rhubarb pie of the spring is a real treat.

Once planted, asparagus also becomes a long-term resident that may live for 15 years or more. Its high nutrition and low calories make it a welcomed guest, so choose a planting area that gets at least eight hours of sunlight a day and has deep, well-drained soil. You won't begin to harvest the asparagus until its third year, and then will only gradually increase the harvest time from a few weeks up to six weeks. The fern-like crowns continue to grow in the summer as they gather nutrients for the roots. It feels luxurious to steam asparagus that was just gathered from the garden.

Strawberries are the earliest springtime fruit. Like most food, the homegrown varieties are much more flavorful than the firm varieties used for shipping. They can be planted in the garden, or in pots or as borders in flower beds. Their "daughter plants" come from runners and provide new plants for the following year. One method to sort out runners is to plant one row of strawberries along the edge of your garden, and allow adjacent space to move the runners for next year's harvest. Imagine yourself picking fresh strawberries early in the morning for your breakfast cereal!

All sorts of berries that grow on bushes will give you an annual crop after you first plant them. We have raspberries, black raspberries, blackberries and blueberries. As with our other fruits and vegetables, we buy what plants we can from local nurseries, and also order from Miller and Stark's catalogs.

Berries do need sunshine and plenty of room, so planting them along borders works well. Most require you to cut back dead canes each year, but some varieties grow fruit on new growth or "prima-canes." These are convenient because you can mow down the entire bush in the late fall and berries will come on the new growth the following year. There are also thorn-free varieties that make picking berries less challenging.

You don't need a full orchard to have fruit trees. If you have open ground, why not plant fruit trees for both food and shade? You could choose nectarines, peaches, pears or cherries—we actually have some of each. Let's talk here about growing apple trees, because they are so popular and can be used as an example.

I realize that I usually favor "old varieties" to help preserve genetics, but I don't like using insecticides, and so choose the newer, disease-resistant trees. Some of these varieties are: Jonafree, Liberty, Scarlett O'Hara, Enterprise and Goldrush. Read about their flavors and when they ripen to choose which you would prefer. You also want to pay attention to which trees need a companion tree for pollination.

Choosing the correct site is important for apple trees. They need airflow, so choose a high location with wind if possible. Drainage is essential, so heavy clay soil will need to be tiled. Apple trees will not grow where there were apple trees previously, because they are territorial and their roots exclude other trees. For this reason also, you should leave about 14 feet between apple trees.

People make a very big deal about the proper way to prune apple trees, and I have never pleased everyone with my method. However, I know apples need ventilation to be healthy, and so I aim for the "chalice shape" with my pruning shears each March. I approach this project with a creative flair instead of a "right or wrong" method, and so really enjoy this early spring task.

I love having fruit from our own trees. We sample fruit as it ripens on the tree, make pies, dry slices of fruit for winter eating and store others for winter desserts. For this reason, it makes better sense to me to sit in the shade of a fruit tree than a non-food-bearing tree!

Nuts, grapes and herbs are other examples of perennials that can give you nutritious and tasty food. Begin to look at your yard as an opportunity to grow high-quality food for your table. Investing now can provide you food for your lifetime.

➼ 18 ↢

There's Always Room for Growing Herbs

"We can't expect to grow everything we need the first year we garden. However, year by year we can add a bit more of the crops we enjoy using. Herbs are a good example of this as we sneak a few basil plants in by the tomatoes one year, and add a perennial sage plant by the house the following year. Most herbs can be started from seed, so they make an economical and pleasurable addition to our garden."

People have always depended on herbs, although today we may take for granted all the ways they enhance our lives. We may no longer rely on them for disinfectants or food preservation, but they still serve as seasoning, landscape, fragrances and medicine. They are inexpensive to grow and give us beauty, lovely aromas and wonderful tastes. Perhaps it's time for you to find some room for growing herbs in your life.

Herbs come in so many sizes and uses, that everyone can treat themselves to one herb or another. No outside space to grow plants? If you have a window that has direct sunlight five to six hours of the day, your herbs will thrive. Choose low-growing plants (so they don't take over your

Although we have below-freezing winters in Ohio, perennial herbs are available most of the year. In this springtime photo, the sage is in bloom in the foreground, and last year's chives are also in bloom farther down the bed. There are basil seedlings planted beside last year's parsley, and the oregano does well one year to the next.

home!) that you can use in cooking. Possibilities include thyme, marjoram, savory, parsley, sage, basil or chives. You can grow them from seed in small, well-drained pots and nurture them with water, diluted seaweed emulsion and sunshine. Pinching off the ends of branches will help your plants stay bushy and provide you with fresh herbs for cooking.

If you have some outside space, many herbs grow well in containers. The closer the herbs are to your kitchen, the more likely you are to use them, so keep that in mind when looking for a sunny place to grow herbs. Herbs benefit from having crowded roots thinned out, so if you know a neighbor with herbs, you might ask for some root divisions. Herbs that can be shared by division include chives, mints, oregano, rosemary, sage, tarragon and thyme.

It's fun to see photos of formal herb gardens, but even when done less formally, herbs make excellent landscape plants. Imagine your walkway lined with rosemary whose scent you can enjoy as you take a walk! Sage, thyme and chives also make good borders, while rosemary or lavender can stand taller by the fence or wide walkway.

I enjoy planting annual herbs in the vegetable garden and always allow plenty of room for basil. I plant it close to the tomato plants to keep predator insects away, and use it extensively in the kitchen for Italian tomato sauces and even pesto. Another reason I enjoy basil is because its flowers attract honeybees and I enjoy doing garden work with happy bees humming around me.

Dill is an annual, but like anise, is a self-seeder. This means it plants itself and will come up in the same place the following year. It's best to distance dill from anise, however, because the two are so closely related that it's easy for them to blend their flavors. That might give your dill pickles a licorice flavor!

Another self-seeding annual is chamomile. I enjoy its bountiful flowers and use them to make a soothing tea. Nasturtiums are edible flowers that are also considered herbs. I enjoy the bright colors of their flowers, the bees use their pollen, and the spicy flowers can be used to decorate and flavor salads and cold soups.

Perennial herbs are gradually finding a place in my garden. Although we rotate the vegetables each year, Echinacea (purple coneflower) is planted permanently along the main path to add beauty. This is important because it makes me want to spend more time in the garden.

Although I never thought of garlic as an herb, it ranks very high at my house on our list of cuisine necessities. We rotate the planting of garlic each autumn when we plant it for the following year's harvest.

Once you have herbs planted in patio containers, as landscaping or in the garden, the next step is to learn to use fresh herbs in the kitchen. You might want to begin by trying new recipes that contain some herbs that you're growing. You can also put some of your favorite herbs in some bland foods like eggs, butter or cottage cheese. Fresh herbs aren't as concentrated as dried herbs, and so you can use two to three times the amount when they come right from your plants.

I like flavoring vinegar with herbs such as dill and garlic. When placed in pretty glass bottles, they are attractive on the kitchen shelves or as gifts. After about three months of aging, you can enjoy the herb-flavored vinegar in a simple oil and vinegar salad dressing. How nice to have something "fancy" that you grew and created yourself!

Dried herbs are usually what you buy in the store as "spices." Now you can have dried herbs of your own for winter use that you know are grown without chemicals and in good soil. When your plants are mature enough to survive trimming, cut branches and dry them in a dark, dry and well-ventilated area. Short stalks and leaves can be dried on screens, but long-stemmed herbs like lavender or mint can be tied in small bundles and hung upside down. Attics or barns often work well for drying. If the drying area is dusty, you can put them in well-ventilated paper bags to dry. They cannot tolerate high heats without losing essential oils, so if you use the oven, don't let it be warmer than 100 degrees F. When they are completely dry, save the leaves or flowers you want to use for cooking in a dry, airtight container away from bright lights. I keep basil, oregano and sage handy for winter cooking in tight containers in the freezer compartment of the refrigerator where I can access them easily.

After you begin working with herbs, you may find yourself interested in using them for teas, medicinal purposes, soaps, candle making, dried arrangements, dyes and even "nosegays." Herbs are a wonderful example of how gardening can make our lives richer and more enjoyable.

➵ 19 ➵

Eat Locally Grown
Food All Year

*❝ People may assume that it's necessary to go to the
grocery store when there's snow on the ground, but you
can store most of what you need for winter meals from
your own harvest. It's enjoyable and satisfying to learn new
skills like canning and pickling food. It's also economical
to save the hard work of your summer's harvest for your
winter meals. Best of all, the food you eat while your
garden sleeps will be high in nutrition and flavor. ❞*

Most of us probably agree that it makes
good sense to eat food that's been grown
locally. Not only is there less petroleum used for
transportation, but local produce is picked ripe
when it's at its peak flavor and nutrition. However,
believing in the merits of locally grown food may
not help us much in the cold months. The CSAs
(Community Supported Agriculture) and farmers'
markets close down just when our own gardens
die in the first frosts.

I know that people survived all year with
only local produce before we assumed to buy
food in all seasons from all over the world. The
rediscovery of some of the methods our ancestors
used has been an annual challenge at our house.
We are gradually learning how to eat all year from

*From top to bottom, this pantry contains—First shelf: vegetable mix,
pickles, honey. Second shelf: dried beans (lentils, Cherokee Trail of Tears,
Tiger Eye, Lima, Calypso, Midnight Black Turtle and Greasy beans).
Third shelf: peaches, tomato juice. Fourth shelf: sauerkraut, apples.*

our little homestead. To do this we both preserve the summer harvest and extend the growing season.

Canning is still basic: I've used the boiling water canner for years to preserve tomatoes, pickles and some orchard fruits. Any high-acid foods can be safely preserved this way, but when in doubt, the *Ball Blue Book of Preserving* gives easy guidance to all aspects of canning. People seem fearful to can their produce, but everyone used to can as a means to have food in the winter. With the *Ball Blue Book of Preserving,* you *can* can too.

This past year was our first year of growing celery, and there was such a bumper crop that I unearthed the pressure cooker from a corner of the garage and put it back to work. Foods that aren't as acidic as fruits require a pressure cooker to can safely. The pressure cooker allowed me to can a concoction of extra tomatoes, sweet onions, celery, okra, bell peppers, basil and parsley in quart jars labeled "veggies." This highly nutritious potion is finding its way into winter stews, spaghetti sauce, soups and chili. No one has yet commented on the uniqueness of discovering celery in their spaghetti sauce!

Canning does take time during the high-yield months of August and September, but lining the jars up on the shelves gives me the same visual pleasure as piecing a quilt, and the same satisfaction that I imagine a squirrel enjoys when its storage space is filled.

Fermenting and pickling add variety: There are a couple crops that take a detour before getting canned, and the cabbage and cucumbers are two that I place first in basement crocks. The advantage of putting cucumbers in a brine-filled crock is that it allows a few to be added each day as I gather them from the garden. After the crop has peaked and we're able to eat each day's harvest, I allow a couple weeks for those in the crock to pickle before I can them.

For the cabbage destined to be sauerkraut, I first cut and salt it, and then put it in the crock and pound it with a wooden mallet. I really enjoy that because it reminds me of my Peace Corps days and the women pounding millet with large, wooden pestles. To add to my enjoyment, I use red cabbage which gives a unique, kaleidoscope pattern with each slice. Non-iodized salt is used when preparing sauerkraut to protect the necessary bacteria for fermentation.

It takes only a few weeks for the cabbage to ferment. I then pack it in quart jars that are processed in a water bath. I would like to have crocks of food in the basement throughout the winter, but I find it difficult not to introduce unwanted bacteria when fishing out portions for dinner.

I sometimes use a more direct method of making sauerkraut and just pack shredded cabbage into clean quart jars, sprinkle one teaspoon of non-iodized salt on top and fill the jars up to their necks with boiling water. After placing the lid and ring on, the cabbage will ferment right in the jar without further processing. Now we have our vitamin C for winter without importing oranges! Additionally, this non-processed sauerkraut has the important bacteria, or "probiotics," that our large intestines need.

A small, old crock was given to us last year, and I couldn't resist pickling odds and ends in it. I first made a brine of water, salt, dill and a small amount of cider vinegar and then added some tomatillos, small pieces of cauliflower, broccoli, garlic, small Mexican cucumbers, Jerusalem artichoke tubers, nasturtium buds and barely steamed green beans. After a couple weeks of pickling, I kept a quart jar of this mixture handy in the refrigerator for meals that lacked either variety or vegetables. Pickling does leech some of the water-soluble vitamins from food, but I would argue that this mixture must have nutrients to spare.

Late summer is a good time of year to buy and process excess produce from local farmers. This not only helps you to have nutritious food in the wintertime, but it helps your local farmers to stay in business.

⊹⊱ 20 ⊰⊹

Additional Ways to Store Food for the Winter

It's convenient to have a root cellar or a basement where canned goods can be stored, but if you have neither, you can still put aside local garden produce to eat in the wintertime. It's meaningful and satisfying to do just one or two new things each year that will get you closer to self-sufficiency and healthier food. Perhaps you can freeze a few tomatoes when they're in excess at the farmers' market. Next year you might want to buy equipment to can tomatoes. You'll smile to see them in the kitchen cupboard instead of processed food from the store.

There are other ways besides canning and fermenting to have local food to eat in the wintertime. Here are three more ways to preserve the summer harvest for our winter feasts:

The freezer still seems essential: The content of our freezer varies with the current year's harvest. We always enjoy the small green beans that are barely steamed before being placed in freezer bags. The pressure cooker softens vegetables, so I prefer freezing them to preserve their texture. My mouth waters now to think of winter meals when we cook them lightly in olive oil, garlic and salt. I've learned to label freezer bags

This season's harvest included potatoes, shallots, onions and sweet potatoes. Winter squash would usually be included in this basement root cellar. Ideally, the temperature would be in the upper 30 to lower 40 degrees Fahrenheit.

so I don't thaw diced bell peppers for dinner when I wanted green beans. Some of last year's peaches made it into the freezer too, but this year I used the water bath method to can them. Shredded zucchini or even zucchini bread is frozen, and makes easy desserts and nice gifts in the winter.

The downside to using a freezer was that our electricity came from a coal-burning plant. We're dependent on freezing for preserving the chicken and beef from our farm, so are delighted that we finally got solar panels installed.

What did people do before they had electricity to freeze food? Smoking meat to preserve it was one option, and a smokehouse was part of every homestead. Canning meat takes energy and a pressure cooker, but then the meat can be stored on shelves. Drying meat for jerky is still in favor, and there are methods that don't require the amount of preserving chemicals that you find in store-bought jerky.

It's fun to dry: Dried beans have become a staple at our house and are a frequent ingredient in winter meals. Many varieties of beans have made their way to us through friends and seed-savers. Whether bush or climbers, we eat or process some in the summer while they're in the tender, green bean stage. Next stage is the shell beans that one can still bite into, and require 15 to 20 minutes cooking time. After that, I fall behind and allow the beans to dry on the vine. When one variety of beans appears dry and there's an extra moment, I cut or pull the vines and put them in a bushel basket in the hot toolshed. They stay there until the slower evenings when I pull out a lawn chair to face the sunset and sit and shell beans into a large bowl. When the chickens head into their coop, I close up the henhouse and head inside for the night. I'm surprised when people comment on how much work it must be to have such a variety of dried beans in glass jars on the porch shelves. No wonder I find it a pleasure instead of work!

Have you heard of Leather Britches? The entire bean pod is threaded and hung up to dry completely before storing in an airtight container. The pod and its beans need several hours of cooking to be tender, but actually have a unique and good flavor. It's fun to find one more way to store and consume more of what we produce.

Drying other fruits and vegetables is an excellent way to preserve nutrients and preserve food for the winter months. I resisted adding more electrical equipment for food storage, but my husband has come to the rescue by building a solar food dryer. Apples and tomatoes are especially flavorful dried this way. To build your own solar food dryer, read Eben Fodor's *The Solar Food Dryer*.

Treasures in the basement: A final method we use for storing food is the root cellar. We built an underground one thirty years ago and found the year-round temperature in the 50s worked quite well for all root vegetables and winter squash, as well as aging the cheddar cheese.

When we moved across the road to the little farmhouse, my husband created a basement root cellar as a substitute for the underground one. It uses one interior cement wall, and is otherwise a well-insulated nine-by-six-foot room with two four-inch pipes to exchange air with the outside. We uncap these pipes to cool the room in the autumn and wintertime, and it gradually reaches a more ideal storage temperature of the upper 30s. An alternative to the pipes would be to include an outside window in one wall. Be sure to insulate your basement storage room well, however, so you don't increase your heating bills in the winter.

A basement root cellar has the advantages of being less expensive to build than an underground cellar. Additionally, in winter I appreciate the convenience of fetching potatoes, onions and squash from the basement rather than outside. Its main disadvantage is that its interior temperatures are higher in the summer and don't cool quickly enough for the usual harvest time. We attempt to compensate for this by planting and harvesting winter storage crops later in the year.

It's a good feeling when you have shelves lined up with canned food and a full freezer and root cellar. You are prepared to eat healthily and economically all winter long.

⇥21↤

Self-Sufficiency through Saving Seeds

❝ Saving seeds from the plants we grow is a very powerful thing to do. Large corporations are buying up small seed companies, and hundreds of varieties of fruits and vegetables are being lost. Planting a few heirloom vegetables in our own garden allows us to save seeds for next year's garden. It also allows us the pleasure of giving favorite varieties to friends, and the satisfaction of saving these genetics for future generations. Saving seeds makes us part of nature's miracle and mindful of how precious seeds are. ❞

We began by discussing seeds and soil. Now let's talk about how to save the seeds from this year's harvest to sow next spring.

I like to save seeds that are difficult to come by in order to help preserve their genetics. Many types of fruits and vegetables are disappearing, and we can do our part to save them for the future. A more immediate reason for seed-saving is to have the seeds you want next spring. I've noticed that it's sometimes difficult to find seeds I want because demand is increasing. It's then reassuring to have our own little stash of seeds from the previous year.

It is a bit presumptive to take a complex topic

This female, open zucchini blossom must be pollinated by a male flower in order to bear fruit. The two closed blossoms already have young zucchini growing at their bases. When they haven't been cross-pollinated by other types of squash, the seeds inside the mature zucchini can be saved to start new zucchini plants similar to their parent plants.

like seed-saving and fit it into this space. However, I find that I'm more likely to dive in and get things done if the instructions are simple. If things sound too complex, I may falter and never begin. That happened to me when I first read Suzanne Ashworth's beautiful book on seed-saving called *Seed to Seed*. It was too much information for me to begin with, but I have since found it very helpful. I want this to be the "primer" version of what she offers.

First of all, seeds from some plants will not grow offspring like their parent plant. Don't save seeds from hybrid plants if you want to grow the same plant. Only heirloom plants will breed true.

Secondly, plants whose flowers have both the male and female parts (called "perfect flowers") are able to pollinate themselves. You can trust their seeds to grow plants and produce like the parent plant. "Imperfect flowers" (containing just the male or female parts) need cross-pollination. When a flower is cross-pollinated, it won't breed true unless there are no other plants around with which to be cross-pollinated. Peppers and all vine plants like zucchini, squash and pumpkins have imperfect flowers that become cross-pollinated. An example is a pumpkin grown from a blossom that was cross-pollinated. That pumpkin, whether hybrid or heirloom, will look and taste like its parent. However, the seeds from that pumpkin won't breed true the following year.

If you do want to save seeds from your summer or winter squash, then you'll have to get as sophisticated as the *Seed to Seed* book. You'll actually tape shut the female flowers and fertilize them with an "anther" from a male flower. That's one way to isolate them. As crazy as this procedure sounds, it's both possible and fun to do. If you're interested, then you're ready for Ashworth's book!

Lettuce is a plant that offers another way of saving seeds, even though it cross-pollinates. We don't like lettuce to "bolt," because it then begins to taste bitter. However, if you allow only one type of lettuce to bolt or go to seed, you can save that seed. Choose a different type of lettuce each year so you can keep several in stock.

Now it's time to talk about what seeds can be saved because they naturally breed true. Heirloom plants breed true if they have perfect flowers to pollinate themselves. If they don't, bees will cross-pollinate them. Fortunately, tomatoes have these "perfect" flowers, and so their seeds can be saved. There's only one exception—potato-leaved tomatoes have protruding female parts (styles), and can therefore be cross-pollinated. You can keep life simpler by not planting more than one potato-leaved tomato plant each year!

Now that we have that straight, the procedure for saving seeds is not difficult. Choose large, well-shaped and fully ripened fruit of each type of tomato you want to save. You only want the genetics from your best produce. For years I saved tomato seeds by putting a dozen or so seeds on a labeled paper towel. They stick to the paper when dry, and I then fold the towel and keep it in a cool and dry place—usually in a zip-lock plastic bag in the refrigerator. If I'm sharing seeds with friends, I have a variety on one square of paper towel, each type bordered off with their name.

Nature, however, adds an additional step to save tomato seeds for the following spring. When a tomato falls to the ground and rots, its seeds under-go a fermentation process which prevents microbial infections. This fermentation also allows the seed to sprout more readily the next year. To mimic that step, put tomato pulp and seeds into water in paper cups for about three days. Label each cup with the variety of tomato. After the water appears foamy or gets a scum on it, pour the contents into a small strainer, rinse, and then transfer seeds to a paper towel to dry completely. Any seeds that float when put in water are non-viable, and you will know not to bother planting them.

Beans are another easy-to-save seed. They will always breed true for you. Let them fully mature and dry on the plant. If it's a wet autumn, take the plants to a protected area so the beans won't mildew. You can later sit with friends and shell and talk, and you'll have beautiful beans for cooking in the winter and for planting in the spring.

After shelling, I put beans indoors on labeled paper towels covering cookie sheets to let them fully dry. I gradually pick out any shriveled beans and debris. Then, before putting the beans in glass jars for winter use, I pick through them like jewels and choose the prettiest ones to be planted in next year's garden. As with all the seeds you save, choose the ones that are the largest and healthiest looking. In this way we can actually choose the genetics we want to grow, and improve our seed stock each year.

If seed-saving sounds overwhelming, then pat yourself on the back if you get some tomato seeds saved this year. However, if you find saving seeds interesting, then Suzanne Ashworth's *Seed to Seed* book (found in "References") will be worth your $25 investment.

➤➤ 22 ◀◀

Extend Your Growing Season

❝ For those of us who have distinct seasons, growing food more months of the year is a challenge. However, when I taste carrots that have been in the ground through light frosts, I wonder if this isn't how they were meant to be harvested. They are so exceptionally sweet and tasty! We might look a bit strange wearing a snowsuit and digging cabbage in February, or retrieving lettuce from a cold frame when there's snow on the ground, but looking silly is a small price to pay for the freshest and most delicious produce in town. ❞

We've been talking about ways to eat local food all year by preserving and storing what's grown in the summer. Let's close the loop now by discussing how to have additional local food during the cold months.

Cover some garden crops: If crops are protected from the cold by covering them, some cold-tolerant seedlings can be planted during spring frosts. Other crops can be harvested after the first autumn frosts and into winter. Row covers (garden fabric purchased from garden supply companies), supported by wire hoops, have allowed us to grow tender plants like lettuce more months of the year. However, it only takes one night of temperatures falling into the lower 20s to lose a precious crop.

This lean-to greenhouse contains summer squash—where the vine borers can't access and damage it! However, we do need to hand-pollinate the blossoms to get fruit. Winter squash has been started by the greenhouse's back, interior wall.

Our cold frame (a wooden frame with an old glass window for a lid) is a bit more sophisticated than the row covers, and has been hauled here and there in the winter garden. It is wonderful for protecting lettuce and carrots from frosts and cold winds. The sun poses more danger than the cold, because a sunny day with the temperatures only in the single digits can quickly cook the lettuce plants if the lid is not propped ajar. I do admit that diligence is a small price to pay for fresh lettuce when there's snow on the ground!

Sometimes, less technology works best. Last winter we ate root crops like carrots, beets and turnips throughout the winter, simply by giving them a good cover of straw. One other trick was to dig up a few heads of cabbage in the fall and invert them into their hole with their roots sticking up to mark their locations. In February, it was simple to dig them up, remove the dirty outer leaves and have beautiful heads of cabbage.

Plant successive crops: If you want a longer growing season, don't plant and harvest everything at the same time. Here are some ideas for keeping your garden going longer by planting seeds more frequently. The following is calculated for a mid-October frost date:

In the springtime, plant tomatillos and parsnips for a late harvest. Both will survive after a frost, and the parsnips will actually taste better.

After solstice, or about June 20th, plant winter leeks in a shaded spot. Give them heavy mulch and fertilizer, and harvest them around New Year's. Rutabagas and turnips can also be planted at that time. Rutabagas are a new food to me, but they are a cross between a cabbage and a turnip, and have a higher nutritional value than turnips.

Twelve weeks before the first frost, or about the end of July, plant brassica, like cabbage and brussels sprouts, for a late harvest.

Ten weeks before frost, or about August 6th, you can plant endive and winter lettuces, like Winter Density or Rouge d'Hiver.

Seven weeks before frost, or towards the end of August, plant kale and collards.

Five weeks before frost, or about September 10th, plant arugula, chard, mache and a spring-spinach, like Winter Bloomsdale.

Three weeks before frost, or towards the end of September, plant lobe radishes for late fall and early winter harvests.

Two weeks before frost, or about the first week of October, plant garlic cloves which will be harvested as full heads of garlic the following early July.

Many herbs are perennials. Mulch your sage, rosemary and thyme—you can harvest them during the winter, and they'll be ready to grow again the next spring.

A greenhouse winter garden: Our big project, both in money and my husband's labor, has been the lean-to greenhouse. It's wonderful to have winter-fresh lettuce, chard, spinach, parsley and peas to supplement the canned and frozen vegetables. The floor is made from compost with wood-plank walks. Because we live at 40 degrees latitude, the tempered, insulated glass is positioned at a 60-degree angle to absorb the low winter sun. A sunny, below-freezing January day will raise the interior temperature quickly into the 80s. We then depend on bimetal openers to assure auto-ventilation. Water-filled plastic jugs, painted black, hold some of this heat into the night. Two water-filled black 50-gallon barrels collect and release heat more slowly. The biggest secret to successful winter crops is choosing cold-tolerant plants like lettuce, chard and root crops. All the information to build and use this project was obtained from the book, *The Food and Heat Producing Solar Greenhouse* by Bill Yanda and Rick Fisher.

The concept of choosing a southern-facing wall and providing a wind barrier does not need to be this elaborate for successful winter crops. A frame with plastic walls can provide crops through the winter, providing the crops you choose tolerate cool nights.

Animals are a big help: Finally, our animals give a big boost to year-round food from our farm. The meat, eggs, milk and milk products supplement the garden produce and help create winter banquets. The animals also provide valuable compost which is necessary to grow nutritious food. Bees pollinate the crops and provide honey.

I'm not suggesting that everyone can have livestock in their backyard, but attempting to buy produce from local farmers rather than distant corporations will help expand all kinds of local produce in your community. Equally valuable is helping to save the genetics of heritage breed animals and plants for future generations.

Calzones

I call the following recipe "calzones," though the ingredients I use would make Italians roll their eyes. Calzones are a baked pizza crust enclosing traditional pizza ingredients. Because I want the stuffing to be from our farm, the result instead resembles the South American "empanadas." Empanadas sometimes have a flakier crust and may be fried or baked. Empanadas also have a varied filling depending on *where* they're made. At our house, this recipe's ingredients depend on *when* they're made. Here's how I make "calzones" in the wintertime:

Begin by making basic pizza dough, then cook the ingredients for the filling while this dough is rising:

Crust:

1 tablespoon honey or granulated sugar

1¼ cup warm milk or water
  (not warmer than 115 degrees)

1 tablespoon or 1 envelope active dry yeast

Stir above three ingredients together and let stand in warm place for 10 minutes, then add:

1¼ cup unbleached all-purpose flour

2 cups whole wheat flour

1½ teaspoon salt

¼ cup extra-virgin olive oil

Stir in these last four ingredients, and then knead by hand until dough becomes elastic. Place in well-oiled bowl, turn dough over so its top is covered with oil, cover bowl with lightweight, moist cloth, and allow to rise in warm place until doubled, about 45 minutes.

Filling:

1 large onion, cut and fried until translucent

1 or more clove garlic, chopped and sautéed

½ cup chopped sweet peppers from freezer, heated through

1 medium sweet potato, cut in small chunks and sautéed until tender

½ cup dried black beans which have been previously cooked
  for one hour, until tender, *or* meat (beef, goat or chicken),
  cut in small cubes and sautéed until cooked through

1 heaping cup grated feta or cheddar cheese, if desired
   (mix in with other ingredients after preceding
   ingredients are cooked and removed from stove)

Assembling:

Punch the dough down on floured board, knead to remove air, and divide in five parts. Roll each part into approximately an 8″ circle. Put a large spoonful of topping in each circle, allowing about ¾ inch clear around the edges. I use the index finger of my left hand with my right thumb to fold both layers of the edge over to the top and pinch down tightly. This method creates an attractive rope edge that seals in the juices. Prick the top with a fork or make small slits in it with a sharp knife. Bake at 450 degrees for 20 minutes.

I like to use a topping or dip with these calzones. My favorite topping is unflavored yogurt that has plenty of garlic salt in it, or pesto that I store frozen. Sour cream or a tomato sauce works well too. Yield: 5 servings.

Enriched Potato Soup

This potato soup has a full, hearty flavor that will delight your taste buds and satisfy your appetite. The chipotle sauce adds a Mexican, smoky flavor while the peanut butter hints of Africa. Whatever its ethnicity, you'll find that the heat balances the sweet for a delicious and highly nutritious cold-weather meal.

Ingredients:

1 onion

2 to 3 cloves garlic

2 medium-sized Gold Yukon potatoes

2 medium-sized sweet potatoes

½ quart of home-canned tomatoes or 1 can of chunk-size tomatoes

½ cup chunky peanut butter (increase up to 1 cup to taste)

2 teaspoons of salt (adjust to taste)

1 tablespoon chipotle sauce (adjust to taste)

Directions:

Cover bottom of large saucepan with olive oil.

Dice onion and sauté in hot oil until translucent.

Add diced garlic to onions and sauté briefly.

Cut peeled potatoes in approximately one-inch cubes, and add to pan. Brown them briefly on all sides.

Add just enough water to cover these ingredients, then bring the water to a boil.

Turn the heat down to a simmer for about forty minutes, or until the potatoes can be easily pierced with a fork.

Allow the water to remain in the pot while you mash the potato mixture with a potato masher or an electric blender wand. Allow some small chunks to remain. Mash in the tomatoes and peanut butter.

Add salt and chipotle sauce. Cook on low heat for ½ hour and then adjust seasoning to taste.

Pesto

This recipe couldn't be simpler or more versatile. I grow plenty of basil each year so my family can enjoy pesto all year. Make a triple recipe and you can freeze the pesto in two standard ice cube trays. When frozen, pop the pesto cubes out and place in a freezer bag for storage. In the middle of winter you can quickly thaw some to use with warm noodles or as a dip.

Ingredients:

2 cups of fresh basil

as much parsley as you like

¾ cup olive oil

¼ cup walnuts or pine nuts (I use "a handful")

½ cup Romano or Parmesan cheese

2 cloves of garlic

salt and pepper to taste

Directions:

Blend all these ingredients together in a food processor until creamy.

Midnight Brownies

These brownies satisfy my sweet tooth without guilt. The eggs, honey and whole wheat flour add to their nutritional goodness, but it is the cooked beans that result in high scores on the nutritional chart.

Ingredients:

1½ cups dried black beans, cooked until soft, or 1
    15 oz. can black beans, drained and rinsed

½ cup honey

½ cup whole wheat flour

2 eggs: place in ½ cup container, beat, and then add water to ½ cup line

¼ cup unsweetened cocoa (purchase "Fair Trade," if possible)

2 teaspoons vanilla

1 teaspoon baking powder

6 tablespoons mini semisweet chocolate chips ("Fair Trade" if possible)

Directions:

Preheat oven to 350°. Lightly spray or butter an 8″x8″ baking dish.

In a food processor, mix all brownie ingredients (except chips) together. Chop on high, until smooth. Clean off sides and blend for another 20 seconds. Add the chips and stir well. Spread this thick mixture into the baking dish. Bake for 20 minutes, or until toothpick comes out clean. Cool for about 1 hour in dish at room temperature.

Frosting ingredients:

6 ounces fat-free cream cheese

¼ cup honey

2 teaspoons vanilla extract

2 tablespoons semisweet mini chocolate chips

1-2 tablespoons butter

Directions:

With a whisk attachment on an electric beater (or with strong hand!) blend first three ingredients until light and fluffy. Spread evenly over the top of the cooled brownies. In a microwave-safe bowl, melt the chocolate chips with the butter. Stir these two ingredients until blended. Using a spoon, swirl the chocolate mixture on top. Allow it to set in the refrigerator for 20 minutes. Serve and enjoy.

Shepherd's Pie

This is one of my favorite winter recipes made from leftovers. When I cook a roast or chicken on the wood burner, I make sure to add plenty of extra vegetables. That way, all the ingredients are cooked and ready to be transformed into a Shepherd's Pie the following day. There's no need to add all these ingredients. Use what you enjoy and have available. Dried beans are a good alternative to meat. I avoid beets because they stain all the ingredients red, but I enjoy occasionally adding a quart of canned apples seasoned with nutmeg. This is a good dish to use your creativity and any surplus stores from the basement!

Topping ingredients:
about 2 pounds Gold Yukon potatoes, peeled
   and cut into approximately 1" chunks
½ to 1 cup milk, a large tablespoon butter and salt to taste
½ cup grated cheddar cheese

Directions:
Prepare potatoes and have them cooking while you compile the filling. To cook, place cut potatoes into cold, salted water and cook them for 15 to 20 minutes, partially covered, until a knife can be inserted easily. Drain the potatoes and mash. Continue beating while adding sufficient warmed milk and butter until smooth. Add salt and grated cheese to taste.

Ingredients for bottom of pie:
canola oil and butter (mixture for sautéing vegetables)
1 pound beef, chicken or lamb, cut into ½" to 1"
   cubes, *or* 1 cup dried beans, cooked
1 onion, chopped
about three carrots, cut into bite-sized pieces
½ cup green beans, cut into 1" lengths
½ cup turnips, cut to bite-sized pieces
½ cup peas or corn from freezer
2 to 3 cloves garlic, to taste
1 cup meat or vegetable broth
1 teaspoon cumin, or sage, thyme and fennel
salt and pepper to taste

Directions:

Melt the butter in hot oil and cook onions until translucent.

Cover the meat cubes with flour, then cook until brown on all sides. If already cooked, just add in bite-sized pieces.

Gradually add the vegetables to hot skillet, beginning with carrots, including beans if used.

Add broth and simmer meat and vegetables for about ten minutes on medium heat. Add seasoning. Don't hesitate to add plenty of black pepper or even a mildly spiced pepper like poblano.

Next, place the meat and vegetable mixture in a large, rectangular baking dish and cover with the mashed potatoes. Cook at 350 degrees for about 45 minutes. For added flavor and color, sprinkle shredded cheddar cheese over the top for the last ten minutes of baking. After the cheese melts, and before removing from oven, broil briefly to slightly brown the cheese. Always cook uncovered.

Versatile Black Beans

These black beans are so full of flavor that by themselves they make an excellent soup that you can garnish with shredded cheese or cilantro. If you cook off more water, you create an authentic Mexican bean dip to use with tortilla chips. I like using the beans as an ingredient in other recipes like calzones or sweet potato & bean enchiladas, because this recipe guarantees these dishes will be full of flavor. You may find using a crock-pot convenient for the longer cooking time that dried beans require.

Ingredients:

1 small white onion
½ head (not "clove") of garlic
½ round of Abuelita Mexican chocolate
2 chipotle peppers from a can of "Chipotle Peppers in Adobo Sauce" (include a teaspoon of the sauce)
1 tablespoon bottled Buffalo prepared chipotle sauce
1 tablespoon ground cumin
1 tablespoon oregano (use Mexican oregano if available)
salt to taste, begin with 1 tablespoon
1 pound black beans (I use 2 cups of dried beans)
1-2 tablespoons balsamic or white vinegar

Directions:

Heat a small amount of olive oil in a four-quart saucepan. Dice onion and sauté in oil over medium heat until translucent. Add coarsely chopped garlic and allow it to sizzle until it turns golden.

Add chocolate and stir until it softens. Stir in oregano, cumin and peppers. Add chipotle sauce. After chocolate melts, add dried black beans with enough water to cover beans. Cook this mixture on a low-boil for two to three hours.

Add salt only when the beans become soft. Add vinegar after the mixture has cooked. Adjust flavor by adding more cumin, oregano or salt to taste. Add more water if needed. No water may be needed if you're creating a dip.

Cook for another half hour to adjust flavors.

How to Cook a Chicken

Different types of chicken require different cooking methods. We found this out the hard way when we barbecued our first heritage-breed bird and found that the meat was too tough to eat. We've come to realize that the backyard flocks are made up of birds that take longer to mature than the hybrid meat birds. Their older, more mature muscles require a longer cooking time.

The chicken you buy at the grocery store is "Cornish-cross." If you raise or buy hybrid meat birds (Cornish-cross or "Freedom Rangers"), you will slaughter them at eight to ten weeks. These are tender enough to cook by any method.

The heritage birds can also be cooked by any method *if* you follow the age guidelines below. In these guidelines, you'll notice that some breeds of heritage birds have the reputation for being best when cooked by certain methods.

Broilers: In general, a broiler is less than two-and-a-half pounds and up to 13 weeks of age. At this age, they don't have much fat, but their meat is extremely tender. Cooking them fast at a high heat is best and so they've earned the name "broiler." The barbecue does a good job with broilers. The Silver Laced Wyandotte breed has the reputation of being excellent for broiling.

Fryers: These birds are about 13 to 20 weeks of age and weigh about two-and-a-half pounds. The meat is still tender and is beginning to get some fat, but using high heat and fat for cooking is best. Voila—fried chicken! Take care that you choose the right cooking oil for high heats. Refined safflower, sesame or sunflower oils are best. As to the breeds of heritage birds that are best for frying, Orpingtons and Barred Rocks lead the list.

Roasters: These birds are about three-and-a-half pounds and are five to ten months old. At this age, the meat has developed wonderful flavor, but has lost tenderness because the muscles are developed and firm. To "roast" a chicken, cook it in moist heat at 325 degrees for 25 minutes per pound. If roasted dry, they need basting. Cooking them breast-side-down works well, but a clay cooker or crock-pot also does a good job. Rubbing oil over the bird before cooking also helps to keep it moist. The Black Jersey Giants make good roasters.

Stewers: "Stewers" may not be a word, but this category is for birds that are older than ten months. These may be the hens that are too old for egg-laying that we don't want to feed through the winter. It's also the cockerels that weren't yet culled. What these older birds require is an even longer cooking time, and "coq au vin" recipes abound for this category. In the winter, these birds can be found at our house in the cast-iron pot on the wood burner. As they slowly cook with vegetables from the root cellar, they make the house smell wonderful and promise a savory and nutritious meal.

Resources by Chapter

1. Why Local Food Is Healthier Food

1. *Local Choices* by Karen S. Geiser and Lisa J. Amstutz, Carlisle Press, (330) 852-1900

2. *The End of Food* by Paul Roberts

3. http://www.motherearthnews.com/sustainable-farming/nutrient-value-of-food-zm0z11zphe.aspx

2. Where You Can Find Local Food

1. www.localharvest.org

2. www.eatwellguide.org

3. www.eatwild.org

3. The Power of Seeds

1. Baker Creek Heirloom Seeds, www.rareseeds.com, (417)-924-8917

2. Fedco Seeds, PO Box 520, Waterville, ME 04903-0520, www.fedcoseeds.com

3. Johnny's Selected Seeds, www.johnnyseeds.com, (877)-564-6697

4. Abundant Life Seeds, www.abundantlifeseeds.com, (541)-767-9606

5. Seed Savers Exchange, 3094 North Winn Rd, Decorah, Iowa 52101, Phone: (563) 382-5990

4. Good Food Needs Good Soil

1. *The Complete Compost Gardening Guide*, Barbara Pleasant and Deborah Martin

2. *How to Make and Use Compost, The Ultimate Guide,* by Nicky Scott

The following can only be found as used copies, but are worth the search:

3. The *Basic Book of Organic Gardening* by Robert Rodale

4. *The Organic Way to Mulching* by the editors of *Organic Gardening and Farming*

5. *Pay Dirt* by J. I. Rodale

5. Groceries from Your Own Backyard

1. *Edible Landscaping* by Rosalind Creasy

2. *McGee & Stuckey's Bountiful Container: Create Container Gardens of Vegetables, Herbs, Fruits and Edible Flowers* by Rose Marie Nichols McGee and Maggie Stuckey

3. *The Vegetable Gardener's Container Bible* by Edward C. Smith

4. *All New Square Foot Gardening* by Mel Bartholomew

6. Gardens Can Be Any Shape or Size

1. *Grow Vegetables, Gardens-Yards-Balconies-Roof Terraces* by Alan Buckingham

2. *Starter Vegetable Gardens* by Barbara Pleasant

3. *The Backyard Homestead: Produce all the food you need on just a quarter acre!* Edited by Carleen Madigan

7. Compost Is Black Gold

1. *Let It Rot!: The Gardener's Guide to Composting (Storey's Down-to-Earth Guide)* by Stu Campbell

2. *Worms Eat My Garbage: How to Set Up and Maintain a Worm Composting System* by Mary Appelhof

8. Planting Seeds Indoors

1. *Starting Seeds Indoors: Storey's Country Wisdom Bulletin A-104*

9. Planning Your Garden

1. *Straight Ahead Organic* by Shepherd Ogden

10. Growing Food without Chemicals

1. *The Organic Gardener's Handbook of Natural Insect and Disease Control*, edited by Ellis and Bradley

2. www.WhizbangRowCover.com

3. *Insect, Disease & Weed I.D. Guide* by Jill Cebenko & Deborah Martin

4. *Good Neighbors: Companion Planting for Gardeners* by Anna Carr

11. Local Food Includes Local Animals

1. American Livestock Breeds Conservancy (ALBC), PO Box 477, Pittsboro, NC 27312, Phone 919-542-5704

2. *The Backyard Homestead Guide to Raising Farm Animals,* edited by Gail Damerow

12. Backyard Chickens May Be for You

1. *Storey's Guide to Raising Chickens* by Gail Damerow

2. *Raising Chickens for Dummies*

3. *Chicken Tractor: The Permaculture Guide to Happy Hens and Healthy Soil*

13. Keeping Heritage Breed Cows

1. *Keeping a Family Cow,* Joann S. Grohman

2. *The Family Cow,* Dirk van Loov

3. *All Flesh Is Grass* by Gene Logsdon

14. Fresh Milk Is a Nutritious Food

1. The Weston A. Price Foundation www.westonaprice.org

2. *Home Cheese Making,* Ricki Carroll

3. Lehman's Basic Hard Cheese Kit, Phone 1-888-438-5346

15. Successful Beekeeping with Your Own Honeybees

1. *Beekeeping for Dummies,* Howland Blackiston (good for basics, but avoid chemicals)

2. *Natural Beekeeping* by Ross Conrad

3. *Beekeeping, A Practical Guide* by Richard E. Bonney

4. *The Barefoot Beekeeper* by P.J. Chandler (top-bar hive)

16. Rainwater Harvesting

1. *Water Storage* by Art Ludwig

2. *Rainwater Catchment Systems for Domestic Supply* by John Gould and Erik Nissen-Petersen

17. Plant Perennials for Food

1. *The Backyard Berry Book* by Stella Oho

2. *Backyard Fruits and Berries* by Diane E. Bilderback and Dorothy Hinshaw Patent

3. *Fruits and Berries for the Home Garden* by Lewis Hill

4. *The Holistic Orchard* by Michael Phillips

18. There's Always Room for Growing Herbs

1. *Herb Gardening for Dummies* by Karan Davis Cutler et al

2. *Rodale's Illustrated Encyclopedia of Herbs,* edited by Claire Kowalchik and William H. Hylton

19. Eat Locally Grown Food All Year

1. *Ball Blue Book of Preserving,* Jarden Home Brands, Consumer Affairs Department, P.O. Box 2729, Muncie, IN 47307-0729

2. *The Big Book of Preserving the Harvest* by Carol @ Costenbader

3. *Stocking Up—How to Preserve the Foods You Grow, Naturally* by the editors of *Organic Gardening and Farming*

20. Additional Ways to Store Food for the Winter

1. *Root Cellaring* by Mike and Nancy Bubel

2. *The Canning, Freezing, Curing & Smoking of Meat, Fish & Game* by Wilbur F. Eastman Jr.

3. *Basic Butchering of Livestock & Game* by John J. Mettler Jr., DVM

21. Self-Sufficiency through Saving Seeds

1. Seed Savers Exchange, (563)-382-5990, www.seedsavers.org

2. *Seed to Seed: Seed Saving and Growing Techniques for Vegetable Gardeners* by Suzanne Ashworth

22. Extend Your Growing Season

1. *Four Season Harvest* by Eliot Coleman

2. *Greenhouse Gardener's Companion, Revised: Growing Food & Flowers in Your Greenhouse or Sunspace* by Shane Smith